Recipe for Recovery

I BATTLED and OVERCAME
an EATING DISORDER,
and YOU Can, Too!

Recipe FOR Recovery

Marina Abdel Malak

GSPH

GENERAL STORE PUBLISHING HOUSE INC.
499 O'Brien Road, Renfrew, Ontario, Canada K7V 3Z3
Telephone 1.613.599.2064 or 1.800.465.6072

http://www.gsph.com

ISBN 978-1-77123-058-2

Copyright © Marina Abdel Malak 2014

Cover art, design: Magdalene Carson

Printed by Image Digital Printing Ltd.
dba The IDP Group, Renfrew, Ontario
Printed and bound in Canada

Library and Archives Canada Cataloguing in Publication
Malak, Marina Abdel, 1993-, author
Recipe for recovery : I battled and overcame and eating disorder and you can, too!
/ Marina Abdel Malak.
Issued in print and electronic formats.
ISBN 978-1-77123-058-2 (pbk.).--ISBN 978-1-77123-166-4 (epub).--
ISBN 978-1-77123-167-1 (mobi).--ISBN 978-1-77123-168-8 (pdf)
1. Malak, Marina Abdel, 1993-. 2. Anorexia nervosa--Patients-- Biography.
3. Eating disorders. I. Title.
RC552.A5M35 2014   362.19685'262   C2013-908183-6   C2013-908184-4

FSC

To Mom, Dad, and Nansy.
Thank you for being my strength when I was weak
and for being my hope when I was distressed.
Thank you for your unconditional love and
for always believing in me.
Thank you for nurturing me back to life,
one spoonful at a time.

"And not only that, but we also glory in tribulations,
knowing that tribulation produces perseverance;
and perseverance, character; and character, hope."

(Romans 5:3–4)

Contents

Preface

Weight. Food. Numbers. Diet. Calories. Clothes. These words are bound to be meaningful to most of us today. We live in a society that often demands that we be thin in order to achieve the ever-so-desired "ideal body." Many people might hear these messages and simply ignore them. But for some, the desire to be thin might interact with genetic predispositions and other factors to fuel up an eating disorder (ED).

This is where my story comes in. If you saw me now, you might never have imagined that I once struggled with anorexia nervosa (AN) and that I nearly died because of it. But looks can be deceiving. Indeed, the eating disorder that took hold of me caused havoc and harm in all aspects of my life. Swept up in the desire to be thin, the illness controlled my mind. Eating was no longer pleasurable but a sin. The scale became my best friend at times and enemy at others, depending on what the number said. Years of starvation took its toll on my health, rendering my body deathly skinny. Reading this, you may be dismayed and feel that this book will be a memoir of my everyday battles with food. But this is not the case. This is not meant to be a depressing tale of my experiences. Rather, I am going to give you an inner look at what exactly goes through the mind of a "starving anorexic," and to help you understand why recovery is such a difficult journey.

This book is not only for those who struggle with eating disorders, although it may be helpful for some. It is also for caregivers, professionals, friends, families, and anyone else interested in learning about this illness—anyone who simply wishes to learn more about the mental illness that causes victims to lose all sense of control over eating and become irrational about weight and food. The information herein is not meant to replace medical advice or treatment; rather, it is meant to give you an inside look about what eating disorders are, what causes them, how they manifest in patients, and how they can be treated.

Why should you read this book? Because eating disorders are real, and I'll bet that someone you know or see might just have an eating disorder. You should read this book because you ought to know that eating disorders cause the most deaths among all psychiatric illnesses.

The first chapter begins with a description of my experience with anorexia nervosa thus far: how it developed and what this illness did to my life. Following this are chapters that explain some signs of eating disorders, as well as the dangers of ED. Once you get through some facts (which are important to know, as they help you understand exactly why eating disorders are complicated and serious at the same time), I will start to talk about my journey through recovery. These chapters are brief and include my personal experiences throughout recovery, all filled with tips and tools to help you or someone else with ED along the way to recovery. When I refer to the patient, I use feminine pronouns to eliminate confusion—but this does not mean that males do not get ED as well. As you will learn, anyone can become ill with an eating disorder, and the information in this book applies to all patients, not just females.

You will notice that I refer to ED as "he." A patient may call her ED a name, but I simply referred to it as "ED." In any case, it is easier to think of ED as being a separate thing from the patient—it is not the patient who is trying to be difficult or ill, but the illness that is forcing her to do so. You may notice that when helping a patient recover, it is easier to say, "ED is making you starve yourself," as this helps the patient understand that the illness is not her fault, nor is she trying to keep herself sick. Caregivers may also find it helpful to refer to ED instead of the patient when becoming angry. For example, you may be angry at the illness, but you are not furious with the patient.

As you read this book, keep in mind the following: EDs are serious mental illnesses, yet they are often under-recognized. They are serious and can be fatal. Everyone with an eating disorder deserves to get help, treatment, and support. And finally, eating disorders can be treated. Recovery is truly possible for every patient. It takes time and effort, but it will come with the correct amount and type of treatment.

The facts in this book are supported with credible evidence, and references can be found throughout the text. I also want to mention that any characters in this book are real, but I have used fictional names.

Lastly, this book is based on my own experiences with anorexia nervosa. Others may have different experiences and opinions. This is not a "heavy read"; it is meant to be entertaining, interesting, and even humorous at times. I have included my own journal entries and thoughts throughout the chapters to give you an inside look from the patient's perspective, or to supplement any information presented. Don't forget to take a moment to make sense of the food puns!

Now, sit back and enjoy some popcorn as you read, because you will be a-maiz-ed at what exactly makes up the Recipe for Recovery.

Chapter One

I won't eat . . .
but I donut think I have a problem

January 2000: I am seven years old, playing tag with my sister. I suddenly stop running because I am out of breath. I take a deep, long breath and feel scared. Why is it so hard to breathe? For some reason, it is as though my brain is telling me to look down. I look and I see my little round tummy. Is this why I cannot run or play for a long time without getting tired? I remember something I heard in a commercial once—that extra fat makes us unhealthy. Am I fat? I ponder about this, but I am confused. I shrug. I return to playing with my sister. But as I am running around, I can't help but think of my tummy and how it moves when I do.

March 2001: It is Easter! I am so excited because my Coptic Orthodox church community has been fasting for about two months in anticipation for this occasion. We have not eaten chocolate, milk, eggs, meat, butter, or chicken in a long time. Tonight, after our church mass, we get to eat all these wonderful dishes! My stomach is growling and my mouth is drooling at the mere thought of eating all my favourite foods again. At church, I hear some of the older girls talking in the bathroom. "I haven't eaten anything all day so that I can eat a lot tonight!" one says. I look at my watch, which I just learned how to read. It is currently 11:30 p.m. I'm a smart child, so I know that much of the day has passed by now. WOW. This girl did not eat anything today so that she could eat a lot at night? Isn't she hungry? I keep listening to her conversation with her friends. "Yeah, I know what you mean," says her friend. "I lost weight during this fast, but now I am going to gain it all back when I pig out. Too bad—it was good to feel thin for a while!" They both laugh and leave the bathroom. Hmmm, I wonder. I am puzzled by what I have just heard. I have eaten all my meals normally today, yet I am still hungry now. So isn't this girl very, very hungry? How did she do that—not eat all day until now? And the other girl—she said it was nice to feel thin. That word. *Thin.* It means to be small—and pretty. At least, that is what everyone makes it sound like. I want to be thin! I want to be pretty! But I have already eaten all day, unlike these girls. How do I become thin? What do I need to do?

June 2003: I am ten years old. (Ever since I was a child, I was always on the chubby side, but I always loved food. I did not eat unhealthy foods—I thoroughly enjoyed a variety of different foods with my family.) On this particular day, I am at a big party for one of my sister's friend's sixteenth birthday. I am spending the time with my sister and mom, eating and enjoying the music. I smile as I put the forkful of pasta into my mouth—it is so delicious! The waiter comes around and asks if we would like anything else. I nod, saying that I want more bread and butter. He smiles and says he will come back with more. Meanwhile, I look out on the dance floor and see all the older girls dancing with their friends. One particular girl catches my attention—she is younger than the others, but just a couple of years older than me. Everyone seems to love her, and they all ask her to dance with them. She is dancing gracefully, and everyone is pleased with how beautiful and delicate she is. I frown. Something doesn't feel right inside of me . . . I feel weird. I instantly look down on my plate and notice how much food I am eating. Then, something pops into my head: *They are dancing with this girl because she is skinny. She is pretty and thin. But they do not want to dance with me because I am fat. No one likes to dance with fat girls.* Then I start to tear up. But I do not want my mom or sister to notice, so I quickly hold back my tears. I stop eating, but by now the waiter has returned with the bread. I do not touch the bread, even though I really want another piece. I tell my mom that I am full and do not want to eat more; but inside, I am dreaming of that soft, warm, piece of bread.

October 2005: It is Halloween, so we are having a party at school with candy and music. I don't dress up or go trick-or-treating because this does not mesh with my religion, but I do love eating candy! Today, I am wearing only black so that I can look "spooky." Our teacher tells us that it is time to give out candy to one another. I walk around and distribute the candy that I brought to school. When I come back to my desk, I find a lot of candy in my basket. I am so excited to eat this—sour patch, gummy bears, mini-chocolates, gumballs . . .! I start to open a candy and am about to bite into it when I hear a voice behind me. "Haven't you eaten too much already, Marina?" I recognize this voice. It is Kate, the girl who always seems to say mean things to me. Kate likes to make me mad. She does this by making fun of my hair, clothes, or things I do. Today she is keen on letting me know that I am eating a lot of candy.

"You are wearing black, today. My mom says that people wear black when they want to look skinny, because that means they are really fat." I stare hard at her, unsure of what to say. I open my mouth to respond, but nothing comes back. I feel the tears coming on, but I can't cry in front of her. "Well, aren't you going to say something? I didn't think so. It is because you know that you are fat. Why don't you dress up like us? Because none of the costumes fit you? Is that why you don't go trick-or-treating? Because your parents are scared you will get fatter than you are now, and you won't fit into the house?" She sneers, points her fingers at me, and laughs loudly.

By now, her friends have gathered around and are jeering at me. "Fat girl, fat girl! Marina is a fatso!" they sing tauntingly. It is catchy, and the boys have joined in. The entire class is mocking me. I can't hold it in anymore—tears rush out of my eyes. The teacher has heard a commotion and comes to silence the bullies. She sends me to the bathroom to wash my face. But the damage has already been done. The water will flush out my tears, but what will flush out the hurt and pain that I feel inside?

April 2006: I am finally a teenager. All of my other friends are slender . . . I am the only one who is a bit chubby. My best friend, Ella, nicknamed me "cow" and even bought me a cow plush toy for my birthday. At first I am offended, but then she says that it is just a joke, so I smile. Meanwhile, there is a boy that I am totally crushing on: Cole. My first real crush. I tell Ella, who says that she will help me find out if Cole has a crush on me, too.

One day, Ella comes running to me, screaming that she has news for me. I'm excited because this probably has something to do with Cole . . . maybe he admitted to liking me back!

"So, what happened? Did you ask Cole if he likes me?" I ask.

Ella looks at me and says, "No. He said that he can't ever have a crush on you because you have fat thighs, and they move around too much when you walk. His girlfriends have to be skinny, not like you. He said that everyone would make fun of him if he liked a fat girl because no one likes fat girls."

I am crushed. My world seems to be spinning, and I feel like crying. Something pops back into my head—memories of my childhood when people called me fat. Memories of wishing that I could be thin, just like the pretty girls. By now, I am bawling my eyes out.

Ella looks at me and makes one final comment. "He says he has a crush on me. He likes me because I have a nice butt and I am thin."

That does it. I run away, longing for someplace to protect me from this world. But there is nowhere to go; I am all alone. As I run, Ella cautions me not to run so fast because "that makes your thighs jiggle even more!"

May 2007: Ella and Cole are girlfriend and boyfriend. Ella is not my friend anymore. I don't have any friends, and I am celebrating my graduation alone with my family. All of my classmates are at the dance, and I am at a restaurant with my family. I eat whatever I want, not caring about what has happened over the past few months. At night, we go to a bakery to have a treat. I see some of the popular, skinny girls from my class. They are having a treat after the dance together. One of the girls catches a glimpse of me and whispers to the others. They laugh.

The next day at school, I see the same girls at recess. They approach me and say, "Yesterday was a lot of fun at the dance. Ella and Cole danced together. All the girls had dates. We all wore pretty dresses and had our makeup and nails done together. Too bad you missed it. But maybe it was better that way, because you know—you are fat. And no one would have wanted to dance with you."

I am about to retaliate when another girl says, "Why were you at the bakery last night? If you are fat, shouldn't you try to lose weight and eat, like, nothing? Don't your parents see how fat and ugly you are? Honestly. You are pathetic!"

This time, I don't cry. I can't. The years of teasing have turned me into a cold, hard stone. Their words burn my heart on the inside, but I must not let them see that. I promise myself that I will lose weight.

June 2007: I am riding home on the school bus when Ella tells me to stick my leg out in the aisle. I do, only to see the other girls' legs there, too. The girls and boys are comparing how big everyone's thighs are. One girl shrieks, "My thighs are so huge!"

I look down at them. She does not have big thighs at all. To console her, I give back the typical answer: "No! Mine are way bigger!"

The response I get back from her shocks me: "You are right. You do have big thighs, Marina. You should lose weight. Eat fruits and vegetables only. That's how people lose weight and look pretty instead of being fat all their lives. How depressing!"

From that moment, I resolve to go on a diet. I get home to find my dinner on the table: a nice plate of rice, chicken, and salad. My mouth waters, and my stomach growls. I take one look at my body in the mirror and I hear all the words from that girl's mouth: ". . . lose weight . . . being fat is depressing . . ."

NO. I cannot eat this meal. I must eat only fruits to lose weight. But how can I explain this to my mother? An idea pops into my head, and I go for it. I tell my mom that as a school health project, we are only supposed to eat healthy foods like vegetables and fruit—for every meal. My mom frowns. She doesn't see how this is supposed to be healthy for anyone, let alone kids going through puberty. Before she can question any further, I try my hardest to convince her to agree. "Besides," I say, "I want to try to eat healthier. It's good for you, and I want to live a healthy life."

That seems to work, and my mom agrees. She watches as I eat only the salad, leaving the chicken and rice behind. I finish the salad and am still hungry, but I do not have the courage to tell my mom that I cannot take part in this "healthy challenge." She offers me the rest of the meal, which I quickly decline. I cannot be that weak. I cannot break my vow on the first meal! She tells me to eat some fruit, but I again decline. A salad was enough for today. By the end of the day, my stomach is rumbling furiously, and I feel really hungry. I know that I can always eat, but there is something stopping me. My brain keeps shouting at me, reprimanding me for even considering eating more. I remember the taunts of everyone who had ever called me fat and I suddenly have a strong urge to not eat. I do not eat anything else that day, and I vow to continue this for a while. After all, what could be wrong with losing a little weight?

August 2007: After a week of the so-called "health challenge," I got bored with eating fruits and vegetables. But the desire to lose weight continues. Meanwhile, I hear that my aunt and uncle are on diets. This particular diet limits everything you can eat, allowing only unlimited quantities of water and certain "no-calorie" vegetables. They take injections to supplement the vitamins that they are not getting from their meals. They lose weight very quickly. It is noticeable; they both look significantly thinner. My mom and grandmother ask my aunt the secret to this diet. She tells them that they must not eat a lot, drink a lot of water, and restrict their intake even when hungry. Almost instantly, the entire family gets hooked onto dieting. My aunt, grandmother, and mom are all eating very little so that they can lose weight. I see the results and I am driven to do the same. When I tell my mom, she expresses concern that it might be dangerous for a girl my age to diet, but she does feel that it is good for me to try to be "healthy."

I begin by eliminating all desserts, because this seems to be what everyone else calls "bad food." I watch as my sister happily and carelessly eats a piece of chocolate. "Do you want some?" she asks.

I shake my head vigorously, almost too quickly. "No. No. I . . . I don't feel like eating something sweet just now." Over the next few weeks, I have become very good at avoiding desserts. My parents have a scale in their room, which now shows me that I have lost about two pounds. I am happy, but somewhat bewildered. Only two pounds? I can—no, I HAVE TO—lose more. If cutting out desserts made me lose two pounds, I wonder how much I would lose if I actually cut out other foods as well . . .?

January 2008: I am in my Grade 9 gym class, at my all-girl high school. Our teacher tells us that today we are beginning the fitness unit, where we will have to do push-ups, sit-ups, laps, and weightlifting. We will also measure our BMI[1] and weigh ourselves.

In front of me is Jane, a very thin girl. She hops onto the scale and it says thirty-six kilograms. Everyone oohs and aahs. "How can you be so thin?" and, "Wow! I wish I could be that skinny!"

It is now my turn to step on the scale. The number is much bigger than Jane's. I hear snorts coming from the girls around me. I try to ignore them, but I hear a voice in my head reminding me that if I lost more weight, I would not be made fun of. I think back to how I have stopped eating desserts. I need to do more, now. I decide that I will start skipping lunch. After all, how hard could it be?

From that day on, I bring my lunch to school but give it to other girls, saying that I always have extras because my mom packs me too much food. The other girls are oblivious to the fact that I am not eating. They are simply happy to have access to more food. When asked if I ate, I reply flatly, "Yes. This is extra food." By the end of Grade 9, I have lost ten pounds. I am thrilled, but it still isn't enough.

March 2010: I have successfully not eaten lunch for the past year at high school. I eat a small breakfast at home, and then don't eat until I return home for dinner. I step on the scale every morning.

---

1   Body mass index, calculated by dividing one's weight in kilograms by height in metres squared. More about this later.

If the number is lower than the day before, I am happy and that means that I am good. But if it is the same or up, I am grumpy, irritated, and a failure. I've become better at restricting, though. I'm trying to eat less at dinner, so I go to bed with a growling stomach. It hurts, sometimes, but something in my head tells me that this is good—that the pain now is nothing compared to the weight loss that will come soon. But soon the weight starts coming off.

I'm angry because I don't know what is wrong. I think back to my family's obsession with dieting, and I remember something about the weight stabilizing after a while. That means that I need to eat even less now if I still want to lose more weight. What could I eliminate from my intake now? Dinner would probably be the easiest to cut back on. I start eating only an apple for dinner. My mother is shocked and tells me that this is not enough. But I fight back, stating that I want to eat healthy. My dad is a doctor, so I use this as an excuse. "I just want to be healthy. Dad is a doctor, and we should be healthy! Why is it such a big deal?"

I lose more weight. My sister starts to notice, and she calls me "anorexic." I am angry. I shout that I am not; I am just eating healthy. My parents realize that I have lost weight, so they talk to me. They demand that I eat more and "fix my head." But they don't understand. No one understands how much I want—no, NEED—to lose weight. I can't stop now, not after all the hard work I have put into this. My parents warn that if I don't eat more, they will interfere. But that means nothing to me, as long as I can keep restricting and losing weight.

June 2010: I keep losing weight, and by now, my parents are furious. My dad announces one day that he will be taking me to a therapist, Jill, who specializes in eating disorders. I don't feel sick enough to have ED—I am just trying to lose weight. Who cares if I am not eating a lot? Isn't that better than being a fat and ugly pig? But I have no choice in the matter—they take me to her anyway.

We have a few family sessions, mainly focused on how my parents must make me eat more. Jill tells me that I have a problem and must gain weight. She instructs my parents to feed me and watch me while eating. This causes havoc in the house. My mom tells me that I need to eat at school; she has asked teachers to watch me. My dad sits with me at breakfast and doesn't take his eyes off me while eating. I am distressed. I feel like a prisoner. Even worse, they weigh me every day, and the weight is coming back on.

I can't stand this. I am furious, and I hate my parents. I hate Jill. But I cannot do anything about it — they leave me no choice. After five months, I have gained about twenty pounds. I can't take it anymore, so I announce that I will no longer be seeing Jill. My parents object because they think that I am still unwell. But I refuse to see her anymore. I hate the way my parents are treating me — as if I am a prisoner who needs to be supervised at every meal.

September 2011: I am starting my first year of university, but I will be living at home. My weight is the same as when I left Jill because I have not had a chance to restrict again. At university, I realize how much easier it would be to lose weight. I am away from home for most of the day, and now I am legally an adult. My parents cannot say anything to me about my weight or food intake.

My first move? Find out how I can ditch my meals. I throw my lunch out every day upon arriving at university. The weight quickly falls off, faster than ever before. When my parents approach me, I tell them to stay out of my business. They are my parents, but they cannot decide how much I eat and how much I weigh. My mom has removed the scales from the house now because she is worried that they have a bad influence on me. But that doesn't stop me, because there are scales at school. I know my weight.

By March, my weight has dropped by about fifty pounds. I don't eat dinner anymore, either. I throw it out. I am eating only a small breakfast and a tiny snack at night. I cannot stop losing weight, nor can I eat again. Food is the enemy; it is scary. Nothing in the world can ever make me eat again. I don't know how long this can last, but I don't really care. As long as I can avoid food, I am satisfied.

April 2012: It is the end of my first year at school. I am really thin. My legs are so thin that I cannot walk on them. I am weak. I cannot find enough energy to walk up and down the stairs by myself, so my parents support me. It is hard to lift my arms up to dress myself. My parents are worried, but every time they say something, I lash out at them.

On April 22, my dad calls me at home. He says that he is coming home now. I wonder why this is so, since he always returns home at night. He yells at me on the phone, saying how stupid I am being for not eating and losing weight. I start crying, telling him that I will change. I have already made an appointment with a dietitian to help me gain weight. I don't want to, but I feel myself getting so weak and tired. I also see how sad and frustrated my parents are. But now, my dad doesn't want to hear it. He comes home with my doctor, who tells me that he has signed a form that will allow them to take me to the hospital against my will. I am furious! How could they? They'll never do it.

But my mom starts yelling at me in a way she has never done before. She tells me that she will not let me sleep in my own bed tonight, that I must go to the emergency room at once. I protest, but it is no use. They will not even let me change into my other clothes. They take me, along with the form, and drive me to the emergency room. Upon arrival, I am admitted after they check my weight and look at me. The nurses are shocked at how I can weigh so little and still be alive. I am so angry at my parents that I cannot even look at them. I tell them that I hate them, and that I will never ever love them again. They are the worst parents in the world.

Meanwhile, I have to figure out how I can get out of the hospital. Surely I can eat a bit in front of the doctors, who will see that I am fine and then discharge me. How hard can this be? I am certain that I will be out of here in a few days.

Chapter Two

Burnt toast isn't my cup of tea

After spending a few days in the hospital, I really just want to go home. My parents sleep in my room, and I make every effort to let them know how much I hate them. They are yelling at me, telling me that this is all my fault and that I am being stupid. They cannot believe how a smart girl like me would stop eating just to lose weight. They think that I am delusional and silly. Meanwhile, doctors and nurses keep coming into my room. I have several IV lines of dextrose running through my veins. I am furious that the hospital thinks that they can make me gain weight by shoving sugar through my veins.

Nurses come into my room and encourage me to eat. They tell me that the faster I eat, the faster I can get home. But for some reason, I cannot eat. I simply can't. Food is scary. I take a look at food and I squirm. I remember how much work it took to lose weight and I cannot even imagine eating. I explain that I am not hungry, or that I already ate before. But there is no fooling the staff. They know my type, they tell me. The girl who has an eating disorder and refuses to eat. One nurse tells me that this is stupid, and that I am going to kill myself. She asks me if I want that. I respond that I am not killing myself; I am just trying to lose weight. She glances at my parents, who look hopeless.

After four days, a psychiatrist comes to see me. He tells me that the medical team has given me a chance to eat and that I lost it. Now, they will insert a nasogastric (NG) tube into my nose to get nutrition into me. I panic. I protest. I will eat! Anything but a tube down my nose.

But it is no use. The doctor comes in and puts the tube down my nose. I am so uncomfortable. I start crying. I hate this. I cannot believe my parents are doing this to me. The NG tube delivers a formula to my body through my nose. It runs all day and all night. I don't dare pull it out, because I heard that doing that might make the nurses restrain me. But I am angry and distressed. Again, I blame my parents for bringing me to the hospital. I vow that I will never love them again. I tell them that they have made me not trust them. But I was trapped. The psychiatrist informed me that he had "formed" me — in other words, he had written up a form stating that for medical purposes, I was incapable of making my own decisions and was harmful to myself. As a result, I could not leave the hospital whenever I wanted. I could also not make decisions in my treatment plan.

Two weeks later, I decide that I am sick of being in the hospital. I decide to eat. And I do. I eat breakfast, lunch, and dinner. I have gained thirty pounds in just three weeks. Surely something is wrong. But what? I am swollen all over. My blood tests come back and show that my kidneys are failing. But the doctors tell me to eat more protein. I am shocked that I have gained ten pounds a week here. But there is nothing to do. The faster I eat, the faster I can get home and restrict all over again.

But things didn't go the way I planned. I woke up one day and felt that I couldn't breathe. I gasped for air and coughed. I felt as though my lungs were restricted. An x-ray showed that I had caught pneumonia. I was given oxygen through a mask. But after two days, I still couldn't breathe with the mask. I woke up, panicking because of the lack of air to my body. The emergency team was called to my room. They made many assessments on me. My parents were scared — they didn't understand what was wrong with me. Then, I have no idea what happened. All I could hear was voices telling me that I was going to the Intensive Care Unit (ICU). I closed my eyes. I was tired and confused.

The next thing I knew, nurses were pushing my bed into a room with a curtain. My mom and dad were crying. I tried to shout for my mom to come, but the nurses wouldn't let her. I started crying. I was so scared. What was happening? Meanwhile, I could not breathe. I heard a doctor saying, "All right. Give her the needle." And then I was out cold.

I woke up in a dark, isolated room. I looked down and panicked. There was a tube sticking out of my mouth. I tried to talk, but nothing came out. I squirmed and flailed my arms. My mom came into the room and explained that I had a breathing tube inserted to help me breathe because my diaphragm was too weak to do it for me. The combination of weight loss, pneumonia, and kidney failure had taken its toll on my body. I cried. I couldn't believe what was happening to me. After three days, I could not stand that tube in my mouth. I demanded that the doctor remove it, using hand signals and writing on a piece of paper. He did not want to remove it, but I insisted on it. It was a huge mistake.

Two days later, I was again gasping for air. Nurses gave me oxygen masks, but it was not enough. My oxygen saturations kept dropping. A doctor came into my room and told me that the only way to save my life now was to insert another breathing tube. He told my parents that inserting a breathing tube a second time meant that I probably would not make it alive, but he had no choice. The tube would prolong my life for at least a short time.

Once again, I was knocked out cold. I have no idea what happened then. But I never woke up. At least, I didn't think I did. I would open my eyes and see the breathing tube in my mouth. But I felt so dizzy and tired. Everything was black and dark around me. I could just barely make out the figures of my mom, dad, sister, and aunt around me. Then I realized there was a huge machine connected to my neck. It seemed to be taking out my blood and delivering it back to me. My parents told me that my kidneys had failed and that this was a dialysis machine. It was trying to do the work that my kidneys could no longer do. I was also receiving medications to help my heart work because it was too weak and couldn't pump enough blood to my small body. This, they explained, was why I was swollen: my kidneys had failed. Dialysis was only used as an end-stage solution to failing kidneys. Simply put, I was dying. I was receiving strong medications to make me sleep because if I was awake, I would feel a lot of pain due to my condition.

And so the days went by in the ICU. I had no sense of time. I was hardly ever awake. But when I did open my eyes, I saw my family and priests from my church praying for me. I could feel my parents' hands touching mine, their eyes looking so sad. I was so frustrated and angry. Why was this happening to me? What did I do to deserve this? All I ever wanted was to lose weight so that people would stop teasing me. I just wanted to be beautiful and skinny. So why did this happen? I did not mean for it to go this far. I had heard that eating disorders could be deadly, but I did not think that this would actually happen.

My life was on hold. And my family around me was suffering. My parents would cry every time I opened my eyes. I was dying, and the hospital staff was desperately trying to prolong my life. They informed my parents to make preparations for my funeral, as I could die any minute without warning. I could hear this, but I could not respond. I was sedated by the medications and I was tired. I felt so hurt inside. I was bewildered by what the eating disorder had done to my life.

My life was over. At nineteen years old, I was going to die because of starvation. I would never graduate. I would never be able to tell my parents how much I loved them. I would never be able to hang out with my sister and friends. At nineteen, the cause of my death would have been an eating disorder.

I believe in miracles, and what happened to me was nothing less than just that. At the end of May 2012, I was taken off of the sedation by a nurse who informed me that the breathing tube would be removed later that day. Apparently, I was doing much better and I was stronger now. My body could breathe on its own. The dialysis continued for about a week more, but—to the surprise of all my doctors—my kidneys had made an unbelievable recovery. They were now functioning normally and no longer needed dialysis. Slowly but surely, my organs and body began to heal. I truly believe that this was thanks to the prayers of all my friends, family, and community. They never left my side and always wished the best for me. My faith has played a major role in my life and recovery, and I owe my life to God. I also believe that the hard work of all the hospital staff brought me to where I am today—alive and healthy, with no organ damage whatsoever.

Does my story end there? No. I was discharged in June, and I was so grateful to be back at home. But, unfortunately, ED was not finished with me yet. While I was sick in the ICU, my organs got better, but I did not receive treatment for the actual eating disorder. I gained weight, but I still did not want to eat. My thoughts were still against eating, and my will to eat was overpowered by the desire to be thin.

So, how did I get where I am today? What caused this massive change in my life? Well, my name was put on a waiting list for an eating disorder inpatient program at my local hospital. In July, I received word that it was my turn to be admitted. Needless to say, I was very reluctant to return to a hospital again. But my parents had made it very clear that they expected me to go to this program and to recover. While my parents had learned some things about ED during my stay in the ICU, they still had a lot more to learn. They felt that this inpatient program would help me and the entire family. Did I really have a choice? Not really. My parents insisted that I go, whether I wanted to or not. Sighing, I went. "Adventures in the Hospital, Part Two" would soon begin. But this time in an ED treatment facility.

Chapter Three

Is it an eating disorder?
Let's taco 'bout it

I arrived at the all-adult inpatient (IP) program at the hospital. They weighed me in a hospital gown and checked all my belongings. My first meal there was lunch. It was, to say the least, terrifying. I was in the program with about eight other girls, some of whom had bulimia, others who had anorexia. Three other girls were IP like me, and the rest were outpatient. I stared down at my tray. WOW. This was a lot of food. It was a croissant with turkey, a piece of fruit, and two granola bars. I was also required to drink a full glass of water. I did not see how I was expected to eat this much. Surely they weren't serious when they said that any leftover food would be supplemented . . .?

They were serious. Before I started eating, the rules were explained to me again. Everyone began eating at the same time. We had thirty minutes to eat. When we had five minutes left, we would be notified. Any food not eaten would be replaced with a Boost supplement. There were always at least two people sitting with us at the table to supervise us while eating. This happened at breakfast, lunch, snack, dinner, and night snack. In between, we had "groups" or sessions. These included cognitive behavioural therapy (CBT), dialectical behavioural therapy (DBT), education group, goal group, relaxation, and nutrition group. Our time was well occupied, with only a brief twenty-minute break throughout the day. We were not allowed to exercise or chew gum. Nor could we drink water or eat anything whenever we pleased. Bathrooms were locked at all times and could only be accessed if the nurse opened the door. The bathroom had a window at the bottom of it to allow the nurse to watch what you were doing inside. Showers could only be taken at 7:00 a.m. or 7:00 p.m. Cell phones were not permitted at all. Visitors were permitted every night from 6:30–8:30 p.m. We were weighed every Monday in a hospital gown. We saw our weights and were expected to gain a minimum of two pounds per week. We chose our meals from a list every week, based on what the dietitian told us we needed to pick. If we did not gain enough each week, our meal plans were increased.

This was very stressful for me. Not having my family with me was different and strange. I missed spending time with them and having their support. Although I interacted with the other adults in the proram, it did not feel as though we were friends. There was often a sense of competition among us, as though we were all against one another. Mondays were always stressful because that was "weigh day." Each patient wanted to know how much the others had gained. Knowing that you gained more than the others was brutal. Feeling that you gained the least was empowering. To someone like me who never found ED to be about competition, this was not helpful. It fuelled my eating disorder, making me more entrenched in my thoughts and negative behaviours. I wanted to be the thinnest patient. I wanted to gain the least amount of weight. I wanted to have to eat the most but gain the least amount of weight. I wanted others to be jealous of how skinny I was. This was a big change from what I was initially like.

Perhaps what I disliked the most about this treatment facility was that families were not involved in the care to a great extent. While I appreciate that the IP program was for adults, I found it strange that families were not encouraged to be around often. For example, visitors were not allowed to be present at mealtimes. This was problematic because it meant that the second I returned home from IP, I was not comfortable with having my family around when I ate. In reality, we need to eat around strangers, family, and friends. By eating in isolation at the IP program, I was not being taught how to deal with the anxiety of eating with others. I understand the reasoning behind this—the treatment facility thought that eating around other people would make us anxious and deter our progress. But I still believe that at least at some times, efforts should have been made to provide us with the experience of eating with people who were not patients with eating disorders.

However, the IP program did help me with some things. I learned that I have to eat, even when I don't particularly want to. I also gained a sense of how much food it was necessary for me to eat in order to gain and maintain a healthy weight. Moreover, the groups taught me about regulating my thoughts and emotions. Although strict, the rules about eating kept the eating disorder in line.

After about three weeks of the IP program, I was at my wit's end. Some of the patients with me were making fun of me because I said that I missed my family. I found a particular patient to be highly triggering because I could hear her exercising in the room next to me at night. Some of the staff members were not friendly and did not show their support for my recovery and well-being. In addition, I felt that my family was no longer a part of my life.

Although I was nineteen years old, I still loved my family and wanted to live happily with them. But my family had not learned about eating disorders from this IP program. No information or support was given to them. This was difficult because it meant that whenever they visited me, we fought. My parents scolded me for being silly and still caring about how much I weighed. I was angry because they had no idea how I was feeling and how hard it was to be living (and eating!) away from my home. Until now, my parents still did not understand that an eating disorder was a mental illness. They needed more education, but this IP program did not offer them any.

In addition, the staff voiced their distaste for my family. They did not like that my mom visited me every night to support me. They explicitly told me that my mother was being overprotective and overbearing. They even encouraged me to tell my mom to stop visiting me (which I did, by the way. But it felt terrible and was something that I would not have done on my own). I was, essentially, being a bit brainwashed. I was shutting my family out of my life and out of my well-being and recovery. Eventually, I could no longer take it anymore. I signed myself out of the program and returned home.

Was that the right decision? I think it was. Some patients may read this and think that I am encouraging them to avoid treatment or sign out of their facility. This is NOT the case. I want to be clear about why I signed myself out. First, I had gained most of my weight back and only had a few more pounds to gain. I was sure that I could do this at home, as I had become motivated in my own recovery. Second, I wanted my family to become involved in my recovery and to help me, yet this program was not exactly supportive of that. Third, some patients in the program were triggering me, and this was harming rather than helping my recovery. The lesson to be learned from this is that you need to be aware of what treatment centre you are entering and what they have to offer you and your family. You can refer to the appendix at the end of this book for details on what to look for in a treatment facility; or questions to consider when interacting with a medical team.

Recovering at home

Once I arrived home from the IP program, I was determined to make changes in my life. I had spent nearly four months in the hospital because of ED, and I was not willing to waste any more of my life on this illness. I had made the decision to recover. I was going to eat, gain weight, and maintain a healthy weight and lifestyle. But I needed help.

The first thing I did was ask my family to sit and listen to me. I gathered my mom, dad, and sister and we had a long talk. First, I informed them about eating disorders. I explained how this was a serious mental disease, and that I was not purposely trying to harm myself. I talked to them about how I always wanted to be thin and how I was teased because of my weight. I told them how ED had taken a grip of my thoughts and actions and how I could no longer choose to be well or eat. I referred my family to useful resources that would help them understand more about my illness. A list of these resources can be found in the appendix.

Once my family had begun to learn about eating disorders, we made a plan together. For the first time throughout this entire struggle, we promised to work as a team against ED — as opposed to them against me and ED. Because of my determination to defeat ED, I took control of my recovery. Please note that while this is ideal, it is not always possible for many patients. Some patients might still not have the desire to recover, and others may be too young to take responsibility for their health. However, it is always desirable to have the patient and family united together to fight this illness.

For example, younger patients cannot always make decisions on what they will eat and how much. Other patients may not have the ability to ask for help when they need it. Meanwhile, some families may not be able to take time off work to be with the patient at all times. Other families may have other children to care for. The differences among families and patients reveal an important aspect of battling eating disorders: you must find what works best for your family and what ensures that the patient will be safe and healthy. This is why having a professional team to help you is best: they can support you and help you find solutions to problems, meal planning, weighing, etc.

Having the support of my family was essential. If you do not have your family to help you, try to find anyone who can do this. If you are recovering on your own, there are some tips that can help you with this, which can be found in chapter nine. I gained all my weight back and was able to eat independently. I was very motivated to change my life, so this kept me fighting against ED. At first, it was very difficult. I hated eating and always felt fat and ugly for doing so. But eventually, the distress disappeared. Whenever I had a bad feeling, I would voice it aloud to my mom. She always listened to me and helped me deal with my feelings. She also reminded me that I was doing a great job, and that she was proud of me. This kept me encouraged and taught me a very important lesson: ED always wants you to fail. No matter what I did, ED made me feel guilty for it. When I ate and gained weight, I felt bad. When I did not gain weight, my parents were disappointed. Over time, I learned that if I ever wanted to live a happy, healthy, and free life, I had to gain weight. No one was trying to make me fat. My parents simply wanted me to be a healthy girl who could eat enough for her body's needs. As time passed, I become more successful at choosing my meals and eating enough. My weight stabilized, and I was able to maintain my weight.

At this point, you may think that recovery sounds fun. I mean, who would mind eating all that they could and not worry about becoming overweight? That may be the case for someone without ED. However, for patients with ED, eating is a nightmare. It is the worst thing you can possibly ask a patient with ED to do. Picture it this way: If you were afraid of snakes, how would you feel if others made you hold a snake five times a day? It doesn't sound fun, does it? This is what patients with ED feel like. As you continue reading this book, keep in mind that while I may use humour to lighten up the mood, recovery was not always easy and fun. There were many days when my parents and I fought. I remember one instance when my mother put too much butter in one of my meals. I was hysterical. I cried, screamed, and refused to eat it. Then there was a time when my father yelled at me for eating too slowly and he said that I was being an arrogant and foolish girl for having an eating disorder. Another day, my sister yelled at all of us for being so focused on the eating disorder and forgetting that we were a family and had to have a life outside of this illness. We also had moments when we all got so frustrated with one another that we refused to communicate. We had many nights when everyone went to bed angry and stressed. Recovering from an eating disorder is a lot of work. It is not simply feeding the patient and helping her to gain weight.

There are many other things that need to be considered. The workload on parents or caregivers is often too heavy for them to carry, and balancing this with their regular work becomes very difficult. Siblings may suffer because of the lack of attention and care for their own needs. Patients feel guilty and fat for eating, and they feel as though they are ruining everyone else's lives. The key thing to remember is that recovery takes a lot of time and patience. There will be good days, but there will also be hard days. At any given moment, you must know that recovery is possible and will happen, but that you need to keep fighting. When someone is ill with ED, every effort must be made to help her recover. In a sense, all life seems to stop until she is better. This can be problematic because life is full of so many other events and obligations.

Therapy can be helpful for families because it provides them with an outlet and a place to discuss their feelings and frustrations. Having family or friends come over or help you with tasks can also be extremely relieving — they can cook for you, clean, run errands, or simply be there to listen to you. Distractions are also critical. During the re-feeding process, the patient gets very uncomfortable from eating and gaining weight. She will also be distressed because she is eating — something her illness really does not want her to do. As a result, finding something to distract her with can be very helpful.

Some distractions include:

● Board games or cards or puzzles

● Movies and TV

● Talking about anything: news, stories, what happened during the day, jokes, etc.

- Knitting or any type of art (painting, drawing, crafts, jewellery making, colouring)

- Writing and reading

- Playing an instrument

- Self care: manicure, pedicure, shopping, massages, etc.

- Playing with a pet, siblings, or friends

Distractions were HUGE in my recovery. ED never shuts up. He likes to keep talking, blaming his victim for everything. He makes her feel awful for eating and gaining weight. He tells her lies and convinces her that she is fat, ugly, lazy, and useless. What I found extremely helpful was to make sure that I was always keeping myself busy. This way, I could tune out the thoughts so they would not bother me. Over time, I learned to silence the thoughts without having to always be busy. However, this took a long time and is challenging.

I still have moments when I feel that ED is trying to sneak back into my life. By keeping myself involved in something else, I focus all my energy and thought into that one thing. It is also an excellent way to accomplish goals or to become creative. For example, colouring was a major distraction for me. It is soothing because it brings out the creative and artistic side of everyone. It also keeps you focused and concentrated on the task at hand.

Another helpful distraction for me is reading. When I am reading, I get involved in the book's plot and characters, and this silences ED. Although I do not own any pets, I found that going to pet stores and playing with the pets there was a very good distraction. Many patients attest to the fact that having a pet or interacting with one helped them relax and ignore ED thoughts. Note that this also means that you have to take care of the pet, so it is not suitable for everyone. As I said before, you need to find what works for you and your family. The patient will find that her thoughts are quieted when she is distracted by a more compelling activity.

One thing to remember is that during recovery, the patient may experience major mood swings. She will feel trapped: One part of her wants to eat and recover, but ED is too strong and makes her feel terrible when she does eat. One minute, she will feel thrilled, but the next second, she may feel awful and depressed. This is normal, so expect it. I found that as I got better, my moods stabilized and did not change as quickly. Again, this takes time. Chapter eight has helpful tips about how to control and express emotions, and this can be very helpful for patients to practise.

You have now finished the first chapters about my personal experience with anorexia. The next few chapters will give you more information about eating disorders: what they are and what they can do to victims. There are some useful tips. But relax! The information is simple to understand. So grab a cup of tea and a snack, because you are about to take a bite into the world of eating disorders.

Chapter Four

Eggcellent facts about eating disorders

There are many types of eating disorders. Perhaps the three most known disorders are anorexia nervosa (AN), bulimia nervosa (BN), and binge-eating disorder (BED). However, it is important to know that each of these disorders can manifest in different ways and along a spectrum in different patients. Also, there are some eating disorders that do not fall into these categories, such as diabulimia, orthorexia, and other subtypes. What is important to emphasize, and what is often overlooked, is that someone can still have an eating disorder even if he or she does not fall into the clinical diagnostic criteria for that illness.

For example, someone might restrict her food intake and lose a lot of weight, but if it is not less than 85 percent of what is normal, this individual may not be clinically diagnosed with AN. However, this does not mean that the patient does not need help or treatment. What you should realize is that eating disorders are deadly, and they can damage one's health in a short time. This is why it is important for patients to be identified—early treatment means that the damage done can be addressed as soon as possible. It is not an overstatement to say that early identification and prevention can prevent death from ED.

So, what are the signs of ED? How do you know if you or someone you know is struggling with an eating disorder? *Below are a few signs or things to look out for.* Note that this list is not conclusive; other signs might be present. Also realize that someone with some of these signs may or may not have ED—this is why recognition and proper medical assessments need to be conducted. If you are a sufferer, review these signs and symptoms honestly. If you are a caregiver, parent, or friend, please do the same. It is not uncommon to be in denial that you or someone you know is struggling with ED. It is, in fact, very common, because we prefer to think that this is simply a phase or a temporary behaviour that one is going through. This may be the case, but it is nonetheless safer to get an assessment to determine if this is truly an eating disorder or not.

Symptoms of Anorexia Nervosa

If you or your child or a loved one is exhibiting any or some of these symptoms, please do something about it! Usually, approaching an individual will not result in any major breakthroughs, as the sufferer will reassure you that she is okay. If you suspect that she may have a problem, it is best to take action: schedule a doctor's appointment, get thorough medical assessments, etc. It is best to err on the side of caution. Do not be afraid to seek help for this person; although she may not admit that she needs help, each day that goes by without intervention is another day that ED entrenches himself in his victims! Please read the symptoms below and recall that sufferers can show ONE, SOME, MANY, or even ALL of these signs. The patient may be in denial, but as a caregiver, you must be aware that the patient is not likely to admit that she has a problem.

● Being underweight or losing weight quickly
Some professionals say that if a patient is not extremely underweight (for example, she is at a "normal" weight or "healthy BMI"), she cannot have an eating disorder. At the same time, some people are genetically thin and do not have eating disorders. However, being underweight, or losing weight very quickly, is part of the diagnostic criteria for AN (less than 85 percent of weight that is expected for the patient). Having a timeline or growth chart can be useful here because it can allow you to see what this person's pattern of weight has been, and when the weight started to come off. (Naturally, there are other abnormal conditions that can account for sudden weight loss.)

● Not eating / "already eaten" / "never hungry"

A patient with ED has a fear of eating because she truly believes that it will make her "fat" or "ugly." Thus, if she can avoid food, she will by all means do so. Just imagine: if you were afraid of, let's say, spiders, wouldn't you always avoid them? The same applies to an ED patient. She might not show up for family or social gatherings that include food, such as mealtimes, parties, etc. An anorexic might also throw out her meals or give them to others because she wants to appear to be eating. Additionally, she may engage in odd behaviours, such as baking obsessively, but never eating anything that she makes and insisting that others eat up.

Be aware of this—even people who are too full to eat something one day can surely try it another day. Claims that she has "already eaten" need to be taken with some skepticism, especially if she is never observed eating. If you are a parent, remember that most children eat meals with their families; if your child refuses, this can be a warning sign that she needs further assessments.

When a patient with ED is forced to eat, she will likely get violent, anxious, angry, and defensive. She will refuse to eat at all costs and may act unlike herself. These are the effects of this terrible illness.

● Calorie-counting

Nearly half the world counts calories because of the pressure to monitor food intake. Many people purchase products that are low-calorie or low-fat because they want to enjoy eating while watching their weight. Other people need to monitor their calories because of health issues. However, there comes a point when this act becomes obsessive. If someone is counting *every single* calorie that she eats, there is a problem, especially if she doesn't need to be doing this. For example, she may have journals in which she accurately documents all her calories and weights. She may even have a "set number" of calories that she has ultimately decided cannot be exceeded. This is a dangerous and obsessive behaviour. A patient may also engage in strange behaviours such as refusing to drink water, believing that this will make her gain weight.

Note that not drinking water or other fluids constitutes a medical emergency because dehydration can occur quickly.

● Failing or compromising vitals

Anorexics might have unusually slow pulses, failing liver and kidneys, low blood pressure, low blood sugar levels, etc. A few medical tests can usually confirm this. Patients might also have very low hormone levels. Although not an accurate indicator of an eating disorder, females may not have a regular menstrual cycle (amenorrhea). However, this sign also needs to be taken with caution because the body is extremely successful at adapting to pressures. What this means is that a patient who is very sick with ED could have a normal heart rate, blood sugar, blood values, etc. This does not mean that she is necessarily healthy; indeed, sudden death is unfortunately common in ED because eventually the body cannot stand any more pressure and fails.

● Pale face; brittle hair/nails; low body temperature

A lack of nutrients, vitamins, and minerals from food makes the hair very dry. The nails also may be very sensitive and break easily. A patient might look pale or slightly "yellow" because she is tired (due to lack of sleep because of hunger, sadness, or any of a maelstrom of emotions), depressed, and malnourished (anemia, etc.). Because she is not eating enough, an anorexic usually feels very cold—even when it is quite warm. This can indicate a lack of body fat and/or nutrients. The body also tries very hard to expend energy on only what is necessary because of the lack of food intake, so certain processes may slow. Constipation frequently occurs because there is not enough bulk material to be eliminated. Note that excessive use of laxatives is also common, and this can lead to dependence, rectal bleeding, or electrolyte imbalances.

● Low self-esteem and poor body image

An anorexic usually believes that she is very fat. She might evaluate her self-worth in terms of how she appears, how much she weighs, what she eats, etc. She might compare herself to others around her, or she might express a desire to look like a thin model or a muscular athlete. She can spend hours in front of the mirror, inaccurately scrutinizing every part of her body. Reassurance that she is not fat is not helpful because her illness distorts her self-image. She becomes obsessed with restricting her intake, losing weight, checking the number on the scale, measuring body parts, and criticizing what she doesn't like about her body.

🍎 Excessive exercising or gum chewing; using diet pills
A patient with anorexia has a firm belief that she needs to lose weight; as a result, she might engage in excessive and compulsive exercising in order to burn calories. This is often difficult to recognize because physical activity is important for all of us. However, compulsive exercise usually is evident if the patient neglects parts of her life in order to exercise, feels irritable when she cannot exercise, or is exercising even though she is tired and has no energy. Excessive gum chewing is also common because it makes the patient forget about hunger and instead focus on chewing the gum. Using diet pills may make the patient believe that it will aid her weight loss. Unfortunately, she may also use illicit substances such as cocaine or alcohol in order to self-medicate or because she believes that it will help her lose more weight. The use of any substance, whether prescribed or not, for a purpose other than that for which it is intended is medically dangerous and can cause death.

Symptoms of bulimia nervosa / binge eating

Please note that some of the symptoms noted above of AN may also be present in a patient with bulimia and/or binge eating disorder. For the sake of completeness, I will also list some symptoms of these disorders here. However, for the remainder of this book, the focus will be on AN. Should you require more information about any of these disorders, please refer to the references at the end of the book.

🍎 Hoarding food
A patient may collect or purchase a large amount of food and keep it with her, or stash it in a hiding place. Note that a patient with ED can buy a lot of food, but this does not necessarily mean that she is eating it. For another patient, however, the purchase of

large quantities of food leads her to binge. A binge is defined as a period of time in which the patient eats large amounts of food uncontrollably until she feels uncomfortable. Afterwards, there are feelings of guilt and remorse. She may then seek out ways to eliminate this from her system, whether that is through the use of pills, exercising, or vomiting.

🍎 Stating that she feels out of control when eating
A patient with BN and BED may feel out of control when she eats because she is concerned that she will eat too much. Causes of bingeing are varied, but may include emotional, social, or environmental triggers. A patient who engages in bingeing usually cannot stop eating, even if she feels full or uncomfortable.

🍎 Electrolyte imbalances; bad breath (i.e., smell of vomit); running to the bathroom after meals
A patient who purges often consumes a meal or food and then seeks out ways to get rid of what she just ate. This is often done by running into the bathroom or shower. This should raise red flags immediately. As well, she may have a characteristic foul-smelling breath because of her consistent vomiting. Vomiting is very dangerous because it can lead to life-threatening fluid and electrolyte imbalances. A common sign in a patient who purges is having scars or marks on her fingers or knuckles, which are caused when the patient puts her fingers in her mouth or throat to induce vomiting.

Remember that ED does not discriminate. What this means is that anyone can develop an eating disorder, regardless of race, religion, skin colour, body size, gender (see chapter eleven) or educational level. I am from Egypt—a country that loves good food. I am also a strong believer in God, and my profession is in the medical field. Nonetheless, I still suffered from ED. Do not assume that someone cannot have an eating disorder because of where she is from, how old she is, or what her occupation is. *A patient does not choose ED. ED chooses her.*

Now that you know what signs to look out for when contemplating whether or not someone has an eating disorder, it is important for you to know what exactly eating disorders do to patients. The dangers of ED are many, ranging from what may seem minor (such as dry skin) to much bigger problems (death). Again, it is important to note that not all patients will have all of these complications. A patient who does not show any apparent problems may still have damaged her body, even if it does not show in her outward appearance. Blood tests, vital signs, and appropriate medical assessments are all crucial because they allow us to determine what is wrong with the patient and how we can prevent further damage. Simply because a patient "feels fine" or "looks normal" does not indicate health; as I have mentioned before, the body can adapt to a certain amount of stress before it suddenly collapses.

ED is a life-threatening disease. I urge you to read that sentence multiple times, very slowly, until you understand the truth behind it. Someone with ED may be malnourished. We depend on food as our life-giving substance: it provides us with the energy that we need to grow and function, let alone engage in numerous activities. If a person is not eating an adequate amount of food (or not properly assimilating nutrients), she will certainly not function properly. The longer she is malnourished, the more compromised her health becomes. Some of the negative consequences are listed below. Not all of these effects are reversible, although some may be. Nonetheless, it is crucial that these complications and effects can be identified before more harm can occur.

🍎 Stunted growth; poor bones; amenorrhea

Due to malnourishment, a patient who suffers from ED may not reach her full growth potential. Although she might have been taller, the lack of food might hinder her from reaching her height.

Bone loss may also occur because of a lack of calcium. In some cases, she can develop osteoporosis (easy bone fracture) or osteopenia (when bones get thinner and weaker), which can contribute to low energy levels, inability to engage in physical activity, stunted growth, fatigue, pain, etc. A bone density scan should be performed to see the extent of bone damage or loss.

Bone loss, as well as malnutrition, can also cause amenorrhea in a female. This means that she may lose her period if it has already started, or she might not get it at the expected onset of puberty. Malnutrition causes a decrease in important hormones, such as estrogen, progesterone, and testosterone

—all very crucial for the development of an individual from childhood to adolescence to adulthood. Secondary sexual characteristics (such as breasts) also might not develop normally.

● Poor concentration; irritability; depression; fatigue
Not eating enough food means that the body is low on fuel. When this occurs, the patient experiences difficulty concentrating on homework, jobs, duties, conversations, and so on.

A lack of food intake also means that she will feel very tired. Although she is physically tired, she may not sleep well because she is hungry, or because the ED thoughts are too loud. A combination of a lack of sleep and/or a lack of food makes us all angry, irritable, and sad. The longer an eating disorder goes on, the worse this gets. The patient may have depression, anxiety, or OCD. These illnesses may be a result of ED, or may have occurred anyway. Either way, it is important that they be treated.

For a patient who is in school or working, the lack of nutrition for her brain means that she cannot perform very well in school or on tasks. Please note, however, that a patient with ED can still maintain a high level of functioning even when she is ill. Her grades may still be very good—this does not mean that she is not sick. She can still achieve high marks because she is driven to be perfect at everything, or because focusing on school means that she has less time and energy to realize that she is actually very hungry. It is worth noting that as nutrition decreases and body weight decreases, the brain also shrinks. Some of this may be reversible, while some of it may not be. Starvation causes havoc in every organ in the body.

● Fluid, electrolyte, and hematological values
Blood tests from patients may or may *not* show abnormal (very high or low) values. Again, a patient may be ill even if her blood work is completely normal—this does not mean that she does not need help. However, blood work can often help us determine what damage has been done. Kidney failure may be evident through BUN and creatinine values. Ketones in the urine may be a sign of the breakdown of fats for energy, which occurs when

the body has little fuel to use for energy. Electrolytes such as sodium, potassium, chloride, phosphorus, magnesium, and calcium may be low. These values are very important because deficiencies in these ions can cause heart arrhythmias, muscle weakness, and even death.

As mentioned above, low hormone levels may signal growth delay, which indicates that the body cannot expend energy on growing because it has so little nutrition to fuel it. Liver enzymes may be elevated, which can indicate liver damage and pathology. Thyroid hormones may or may not be low, meaning that the basal metabolism in the body is slowed because of a lack of energy. Decreased thyroid hormones can lead to lower body temperature, fatigue, and weakness. The B vitamins may be low, indicating a lack of nutrition.

Note that this list is not conclusive; a professional medical team should perform a complete blood test to see what problems are present.

❦ Heart changes

Although the heart can adapt to a certain amount of stress, it eventually fails and can no longer sustain life. An ECG should be performed to see how the heart is functioning. Usually, patients will have bradycardia (low heart rate) and may have abnormal heartbeats. These are serious and life-threatening complications, as death can occur unexpectedly. If the patient has heart disturbances, bed rest may be necessary. The heart might experience a loss of muscle mass due to starvation, and it might not be able to beat properly because of electrolyte imbalances. Death is not uncommon.

❦ Pregnancy and risks to the fetus

We must also consider what happens when a female is pregnant and is struggling with ED. First, recall that many females with ED might not menstruate, which will prevent pregnancy. However, should a patient become pregnant, there are many risks to herself and to the growing fetus. The most obvious problem is that if the woman is not eating enough, she will not have enough nutrition for herself, let alone a growing baby. A pregnant woman requires extra calories, vitamins, and minerals. This means that any intake will go toward keeping the mother alive, which results in less nutrition to the fetus. This may result in growth restriction, deformities, preterm delivery, and a low birth weight baby. Furthermore, the relationship between folate intake and neural tube defects in babies is strong. If the mother is not consuming enough foods with folate (and is not getting supplements), the baby could be born with defects such as spina bifida.

Moreover, studies have found that insufficient caloric intake in the mother is related to an increased risk of miscarriage or stillbirth. Think about what happens to the patient when she is not eating enough: she is tired and weak, and her bodily functions do not occur properly. Now, imagine how much more serious this will be for a growing baby! What is also important to consider is that even after delivery, the baby may still be affected by the mother's ED. For example, insufficient food intake may reduce the mother's supply of breast milk. Furthermore, having ED is correlated with postpartum depression, a serious mental state that occurs after delivery of the baby. Postpartum depression can be debilitating, as the mother often does not have enough energy or motivation to take care of herself or her baby.

Finally, while research is still occurring on the topic of genetics and ED, there has been found to be a component of inheritability with regards to developing ED. Let me be clear about this: having an ED does not automatically mean that your child will have an eating disorder as well; however, it does mean that the child may be at *greater risk* of having an ED. Why does this happen? To be honest, there is a still a lot we don't know about eating disorders and why they occur. Research is being conducted to see if there are any risk genes or chromosomes associated with eating disorders. I know of many parents who had ED and were able to recover either before becoming parents, or during parenting. The important thing to remember is that there could be a genetic component in the etiology of eating disorders, and that seeking treatment immediately is essential.

I realize that was a lot of information you just read. It is overwhelming, isn't it? You might want to go back and take another look at it. It is critical that you understand how serious eating disorders are. Equally important is the need to address any warning signs or complications. As I mentioned before, patients will typically not admit to having a problem. This was definitely the case for me. I denied any problems, saying that I was always full, not hungry, or already ate. I was functioning normally; my marks in school remained very high and did not suffer. Even when I was very weak and could not walk, I made excuses and denied having any pain or weakness. For a time, my blood work was also normal, as were my vital signs. But this quickly changed and the eating disorder did increasingly more damage to my body and organs.

Remember that the outside might look normal even though severe internal harm is occurring. Also remember that confronting a patient may not go as you planned. Very rarely do patients admit having a problem and agree to get help. This means that as a parent, friend, or caregiver, it is your job to encourage her to get help. If the patient still refuses, it may even be necessary to get help for her.

As a parent or friend, you may have to do things that you really do not want to do, such as bring the patient to the hospital or take her out of school. It will hurt you to do this, and you may doubt that what you are doing is the right thing, but be assured that any eating disorder, no matter how small or big, is a life-threatening illness and is worth any effort you might make. Each day that goes by without treatment for ED is another full twenty-four hours of organ damage, chemical abnormalities, and emotional damage for the patient.

Do not expect for a patient to be grateful or ecstatic that you are making her get treatment. On the contrary, she will scream, deny, yell, and may even be violent. If this occurs, you are likely doing something that the eating disorder does not want to happen. In a sense, seeing resistance may very well mean that you are doing the *right* thing—you are calling attention to the disorder that is robbing the patient of her health. Even when she is deathly ill, she may not see ED as being particularly dangerous or harmful. She will more often than not side with ED and blame you for ruining her life by seeking treatment. She may say things to you that you have never heard her say before, such as hateful words or harsh insults. Again, rest assured that this is NOT the patient. It is the eating disorder that is lashing out at you because it is angry that you are putting a stop to its control over the patient.

When I was ill, I promised that I would hate my parents for the rest of my life, and that I would never forgive them for making me eat and bringing me to the hospital. But today, I realize that my parents have saved my life. They helped me when I was unable to help myself. They stood strong and brave in front of ED when I was not able to do so. They challenged ED when I could not do the same. They fought for my life when I was unaware that ED was taking it from me.

The patient might not say these things to you, but she will eventually feel grateful. It will take time. Do not expect for the patient to undergo a sudden change of heart and mind during treatment. It might be years before she is actually motivated to recover. During this time, it is important for recovery to continue, despite the wishes of the patient. She may not realize that she needs to recover, so you need to be the strong one in the situation. She might not tell you how thankful she is that you are saving her life but she might feel it. One day, the patient may just tell you how grateful she is that you interfered and helped her. It could take months or years, but I guarantee that she will be thankful. She may express this in different ways, such as writing notes, saying it aloud, or simply smiling at you. But inside, she will know that you did something that she could not do alone—you saved her from the trenches of ED, from the horrible and painful battle of starvation.

If you discover that someone you know has ED, it can be really scary. You might be confused as to *why* the patient is ill, why she is acting this way, and why she just can't eat! If your friend has ED, you might be willing to do anything to help, but you are confused as to what you can actually do. Having anorexia has made me somewhat more aware of the things that helped, and those that did not help me while I was sick. Read this and see which statements you have used before or might say.

What not to do/say

- 🍎 "You look really thin. You need to eat something." (Victim will get defensive and feel offended that you are telling her to eat.)

- 🍎 "WHY CAN'T YOU JUST EAT?" (I can't "just eat" because I have an illness that prevents me from eating. Why can't cancer patients just kill their cancer cells? Point proven.)

🍎 "Do you have cancer or something?" (In a sense, ED *is* kind of like cancer. Hearing this made me feel like the other person was mocking me—it was obvious that I was sick, so why were people asking?)

🍎 "Just ignore the eating disorder. You are going to die." (Well, you are right. This can kill me. But telling me to ignore it is undermining the complexity of the illness. It takes a lot more than just "ignoring" ED to recover.)

🍎 Instead of telling the victim to go and eat something— which she will certainly NOT do—try asking her if she would like to have a meal with you. Maybe this will ease her anxiety. If she declines, don't keep pushing. The patient is not trying to be rude; she is just scared, and ED is screaming at her.

🍎 Don't stop inviting her to parties or get-togethers just because she always says no. The victim's ED wants to isolate her. If you stop inviting her to gatherings, ED will take more advantage of this and tell her that she is not welcome with her friends because she is useless, fat, ugly, etc.

🍎 Don't call any of her symptoms or behaviours "stupid." Saying that starvation is stupid does not help the victim—it only makes her feel bad about herself and even less confident.

What can be helpful

🍎 When the time is right, approach the person and say that you are worried. You have noticed that she looks a bit different or ill, and you want to know how you can help her. The victim will usually take this as a supportive approach.

🍎 Ask the person if you can help her find resources. Maybe you can drive her to a doctor's appointment or go to see a dietitian or therapist.

- ❧ Offer to take her out for a small snack or meal. If she refuses or declines, make another commitment to do something with her. Sometimes, the patient will agree to a gathering, and maybe this can encourage her to stop isolating herself from others.

- ❧ Let her know that getting treatment for her eating disorder is not wrong or shameful. It is an illness like any other. Getting professional help — in any form — is important. Tell her that you are there for her: To support, to love, to care, to do whatever you can.

- ❧ Check in with the victim often. Give her a call to ask if she is all right. Make her feel loved and important. This can help her self-esteem and made her feel less isolated.

Keep in mind that sometimes, no matter what you say or do, a patient may not want to talk about it. She may deny having a problem, refuse help, or ignore your help. Remember that ED is a mental illness and causes patients to have a distorted and inaccurate view of how they really look. When I was ill, I denied having a problem because I truly did not see an emaciated person when I looked in the mirror. Anorexics usually struggle with this.

There is actually research showing that anorexics do not see themselves the same way that others do. The visual cortex in an anorexic seems to be less active when looking at herself versus when she looks at others.[2] What does this mean? In simple terms, it means that when a patient with ED looks at herself, she cannot see that she is thin. Her brain, for some reason, is wired this way. This is called "anosognosia" — the inability to see that one is very ill. Note that this is not a defence mechanism like denial; rather, it is a result of changes in brain functioning. This is why a patient often cannot seek help for herself — she literally cannot see how ill she is.

All is not hopeless, though. Evidence does show that as victims recover, the brain responds accordingly, and they begin to see things as they really are. This is one reason why a patient's recovery gets easier as

---

2   S. Guisinger, *Anorexia Nervosa: A Guide for Anorexics and Their Loved Ones* (Missoula, MT: Creative Copy, 2008).

time goes on — her brain begins to recover as well, and she becomes free of ED's hold.

If you are a patient who is struggling with ED, you may think that you are not "sick enough" to have ED, or that others are making a big fuss over your body without any evidence. You may look into the mirror and truly believe that you are not ill. However, remember that ED is a mental illness and thus changes some aspects of thinking and behaviours. If someone is worried about you and tries to approach you, do not take it with a grain of salt. Remember that right now, your brain might not see your body the way it really is, but others can. Do not become defensive or try to deny your problems. Admitting that you need help is the first step toward recovery.

Things to consider . . .

Do I, or does someone I know, exhibit any of the signs and symptoms of ED listed above? Which ones? Is the patient happy with her weight? Does she make attempts to control her weight through food intake, diet pills, laxatives, exercise, etc.?

1. Does the patient admit to having a problem? Is she willing to get treatment?

2. Can you pinpoint any damage that has already occurred?

3. Is the patient being followed by a medical team that can address health issues?

4. What are the patient's blood values, ECG results, etc.? Are they being monitored?

And don't forget: all eating disorders are life-threatening and deserve treatment!

Chapter Five

ED, you butter back off

Dealing with an eating disorder is a life-changing challenge. Regardless of the age of the victim, it is a scary and difficult experience. Eating disorders can target anyone—girl or boy, young or old, short or tall . . . So, you have determined that your child has a problem with eating, weight, or food. Now what?

The first step is to get medical attention. Take the patient to the doctor, explain what is occurring, and ask that the patient be monitored. It sounds easy enough, right? Well, the problem is that many physicians are unaware of what eating disorders are, how they should be treated in practice, and what to do for them. Many doctors might not see a problem, especially if the patient is not underweight or is medically stable. BUT YOU KNOW YOUR CHILD BEST. If you believe there is a problem, follow your instincts. If it is possible, educate the medical personnel so that they can help you. If not, you need to find a medical team that understands eating disorders and can help the patient.

Another problem that often arises is when the patient is considered an adult, and so doctors are not willing to speak to her in your presence. This is also problematic because of the issues of confidentiality, whereby physicians will not disclose any information to you because of the patient's age. There are ways to get around this, however. First, reinforce the fact that the patient is ill, and that as a parent, you need to know what is occurring so that you can help your child. Second, it may be helpful for you to apply for "guardianship" (or whatever else it is called where you live). This basically means that you are stating that since the patient has a health issue and cannot help herself, you are to be in charge of her. Note that this process can be long and difficult. It is, of course, much simpler to find a medical team that believes in family involvement from the beginning, as this empowers parents to help their children. It is always a good idea to ask the medical team about their approaches when dealing with eating disorders, as is mentioned in the appendix.

Now that you've gotten the patient to a team, what happens next? First, certain assessments need to be performed. Vital signs should be taken, blood drawn, ECGs and bone scans performed. A thorough health history, including past medical history, medications, and family history is also important. It may be helpful for you to indicate the progress of the eating disorder: when you noticed it, how the patient has changed since you noticed the disorder, what her eating habits are, etc. Anything you can provide detail about is important because it can help the team decide what the patient needs.

The decision to treat the patient has been made. Now comes the hardest part: making a treatment plan and implementing it. You should ask questions whenever you are unsure or confused about something. Always trust your gut and let the team know what you are thinking and feeling. Make sure that the plan you are making is feasible, doable, and workable for you and the family. Also ensure that the plan will be successful in that the patient understands what is expected of her, and that the team is willing to support you. If you are dealing with a young adult, it may help to get her input for the plan. (This may not always work, especially if she is very ill and unwilling to participate.)

Let's assume that the patient will be treated at home. How do you know what a good plan is? What should the plan include information about? What should you expect from the medical team? Below are some things to consider when formulating a plan of action to fight the eating disorder.

🍎 What is the patient's weight now? How much weight does she need to gain? This is usually based on a BMI calculator for children or adults, depending on what age the patient is. Growth charts can be useful because they help track the patient's growth pattern.

How much weight should the patient gain per week? Typically, one to two pounds is the desired range. Any less might not be fast enough, and any more might indicate complications. However, during the first few weeks, weight is usually quickly regained because the body is so dehydrated and holds onto anything it is given. This will slow down over time. See chapter seven for details.

🍎 Who will be responsible for buying, planning, and preparing meals? Is this feasible for the caregivers? For example, parents are often told to "feed the patient" but they are not told how to do this. This can be hard for some parents because they are confused as to how much food patients need to gain weight. A dietitian specializing in eating disorders can be very helpful here. However, it is important to note that parents need to be involved in this process because they are aware of what groceries they have access to, how much money they can spend, what foods they can prepare, etc.

If applicable, patients can be asked to help with this. You need to be careful, though, because many patients find food highly anxiety-provoking and will not be able to discuss anything related to food. What this means is that if the patient is ABLE to list foods she is willing to eat, this can be incorporated into the menu. However, the patient should not be permitted to restrict a wide variety of foods — all foods are important to restore her health.

It might be helpful to actually see the dietitian without the patient first in order to gain an understanding of what the menu should look like. Afterwards, the patient can help decide what foods can be added to the plan (if she is mentally and emotionally able to do this; many patients cannot be involved in choosing foods because it makes them anxious, angry, and terrified). It is important to note that the patient should not typically be allowed to choose her portions because she will often choose too little. As time progresses, the goals of treatment will include helping her learn how much is enough, but in the early stages of recovery, this is not the initial focus.

🍎 What is a good way to present food to the patient? Many treatment facilities use the concept of "Magic Plate," whereby parents or caregivers prepare the food and serve it to the patient. It is expected that the patient consume the entire meal. This concept is helpful because it empowers parents to take control over the patient's eating disorder and to feed them enough.

However, this does put a lot of responsibility on the parent. It often means that parents must take time off work to be with the patient at all meals to ensure that everything is consumed and retained. Don't be shocked to hear this—the patient can find ways to not eat, even when she is right in front of you. She can hide food in pockets, napkins, her hair, clothes, etc. She is not trying to deceive you; rather, she is scared of eating, and it is ED that is pushing her to do so. That is why in the early stages (and sometimes for a long time after), the patient needs to be monitored during mealtimes. After she eats, you need to ensure that she will not purge or exercise excessively to burn the calories she just ate. Whatever method you use, make sure that your treatment team supports you in it. Ensure that the patient understands that her job now is not to worry about anything else other than recovering. She is to sit down for meals and eat. Make use of distractions during mealtimes, as it is very distressing for her to eat.

🍎 What happens if the patient does not eat or gain weight? This is one of the hardest parts of making and implementing a plan of action. You've prepared and presented the food, and the patient is refusing to eat. What happens now? Usually, parents use a phrase such as, "Life stops until you eat." This means that until she eats, her life is on hold. If she is too sick to eat, she is clearly too ill to be playing, going to school, working, or reading.

Again, this is easier said than done. A problem arises when the patient gets physical or violent and still refuses to eat. When this happens, you need to know how your treatment team will respond. Can you take the patient to the hospital if she refuses to eat? Does she need to stay home for the rest of the day? Make sure that whatever you plan on doing, it is enforceable.

I want to emphasize that this does not mean you are punishing the patient. She cannot just choose to eat—the ED is simply too strong and mean. You are not reprimanding her for her illness; rather, you are letting her know that even though the ED is trying to kill her, you will not allow this to happen. You will not be pushed around and bullied by ED, which is stopping the patient from eating. ED will not be allowed to control the family, the parents, or the patient. You are in control now. Until she can master the ability to control ED, you must do it for her.

If the patient does not gain weight, the food amounts in the meal plan may have to be increased. Remember that the patient with ED needs to eat a great amount of food to gain weight: the food goes to healing the damaged organs, making cell membranes, synthesizing hormones, repairing any chemical imbalances, and actually providing her with energy to stay alive. This translates into a lot of food.

Now, what DO you feed the patient? We know that we need to get her to eat, but do you feed her just *anything at all?* Fast food included? Fruits and vegetables? This is also a hard part of making a plan because we must realize that an ED patient does not want to eat, and she will feel full quickly. The starvation that she has endured for so long literally shrinks her stomach so that she cannot hold a lot of food at one time. Now comes one of the most common questions when recovering from ED: How does the patient eat enough food to gain weight when she is not hungry and cannot eat a lot at a time? Here we come across the famous phrases, "quality, not quantity" and "big-footprint" foods. What do they mean? They mean that as a caregiver, you can prepare meals that will pack a punch, so to speak, without filling the patient too much. How do you do this? Make use of ingredients that are calorie-dense. You can add butter and oil to sauces, breads, and muffins. You can use whole cream for smoothies, cereals, and drinks. Use whole-fat milk, ice cream, and yogurt. Buy the most calorie-dense bread you can find. Add whole or shredded nuts to oatmeal, parfaits, and baked goods.

MARINA ABDEL MALAK ● 46

Many people read this and think of potential problems:

1. What if the patient notices how I am cooking and preparing meals with this calorie and fat content?

2. What if I am on a tight budget and cannot afford to buy and cook like this?

3. What if I give the patient too many calories and she gains the weight too fast?

4. What if we never ate like this before — is it still reasonable to expect the patient to eat this way now?

I'll bet you are just craving (ha-ha) the answers, so let's eat away at them!

1. The benefit of using "Magic Plate" is that the patient typically is not present when you are preparing meals. This way, she cannot see what you are putting into the food. Is this being disloyal and lying? No. You are simply giving her what she needs to be alive and healthy. Are you tricking her? No. If she asks if there is (for example) butter in the dish, you have two options. You can either tell her that you have made it the way you and the team have decided, and it is her job to eat without worrying about what is in it. Or, you can simply tell her that there is butter, and that instead of worrying about what is in it, she should simply eat. What you choose to say or do depends on your style, personality, and what the treatment plan says.
    As a patient at home, I always asked my mom what she put in it. I could taste nearly everything and was sure that she had loaded my food with oil. At first, she did not know what to say. When she responded with "I am giving you what you need," I went ballistic. I hollered, yelled, and panicked. When she told me that she had put butter in it, I did the same. It seems like a lose-lose situation, right? There is no right answer to this question. Some parents learn to ignore the patient because they realize that it is ED asking all the questions. Others respond

with vague answers. Still others tell the patient what is in the food. Just know that whatever you decide to do, the patient will still probably not want to eat it. And that is normal for patients with ED.

Sit calmly with her and coach her through it. Use distractions, but be firm. The food has got to be eaten. All of it. She needs this for her life. Once she eats, she can do other things.

2. Having a limited amount of money to spend on groceries is really hard because cooking for a patient with ED requires food in large quantities, as well as variety. If possible, try to relieve yourself from other expenses such as luxury items. All of that can wait until your child gets better. If you are still on a tight budget, try asking others for help. You will be surprised at the amount of love, kindness, and care you can receive from others. Perhaps family members can bake food for you according to your recipes or instructions. Maybe your friends can pitch in to buy some groceries for you. Some parents have even found that they can claim their grocery bills as a health expense on their taxes. Another smart option is to buy the alternative (i.e., not brand name) product of what you are looking for. In most cases, it makes no difference whether the bread is from the store's own bakery or from some big, popular company. If the nutrition — calories, vitamins, minerals, serving size, and so on — is the same, and it tastes the same, but the price is cheaper, by all means buy what is least expensive!

3. Oh, the dreaded "rate of weight gain" question. This is a popular concern among patients and caregivers, and rightly so. We all want the patient to be healthy, but we by no means want to make her overweight or unhealthy. This is why having a medical team with experience with ED is important — they can help you monitor progress and adjust the meal plan as needed. A weight gain of two to ten pounds is common for the first week because the body is very dehydrated. However, this should slow down and even out to about one to two pounds a week. If for some reason the weight gain is more, your team should be able to help you determine why this is so.

There IS a risk of feeding too much and too quickly — this is called "re-feeding syndrome" and it can be life-threatening. Re-feeding syndrome can occur in any patient who has not been eating enough for around five days. To keep it simple, the offending agent is phosphorus. During periods of starvation, phosphorus is depleted. When one eats again, this pushes more phosphorus into cells, further decreasing blood levels. This can cause convulsions, weakness, and even death. This is why the patient must be monitored by a medical team. In any case, after the risk of re-feeding syndrome is over, the patient should gain about one to two pounds a week.

If the team is concerned about rapid weight gain, they may change the meal plan. It is equally important for you, as a caregiver, to not be dismayed by the weight. For patients, it is hard to see the weight come back on quickly. For some parents, this may be hard because the patient's fear of becoming overweight starts to get to you. You have a right to be scared — after all, you have promised her that you will not make her overweight or "fat." However, keep in mind that the patient will not become "fat" just because she has gained weight quickly. The body is desperate for food and it needs a lot of it. When the patient is nearing her goal weight, the meal plan may be altered again to help her maintain and not gain excessively. But at the beginning, focus on your one goal: to feed the patient enough to gain what is necessary for her health.

4.   Many caregivers ask the same question: What if we never use butter, oil, or whole cream? Is it right for us to introduce this now into the patient's menu? Are we being hypocrites by telling her that all food is good, but we won't eat what she eats?

First, remember that the needs of a patient who is eating to gain weight are much greater than that of a parent who is around forty years old. Furthermore, the patient is eating to restore health; you already eat enough for your own well-being. If possible, try explaining this to her — it may help her grasp why not everyone is eating what she is. In many cases, however, it is ideal for the entire family to eat the same thing. This shows the patient that no food is "bad food," and that she is not eating something that you yourself wouldn't dare touch.

But how can you do this without gaining weight and making your family gain as well? A useful strategy is to make everyone the same meal, but to add the "extras" only to the patient's meal. For example, you can make one pot of pasta sauce, but then add oil only to the patient's portion. Alternatively, some families find that they have to eat what the patient does or she refuses to touch anything. In such a case, you may find that you have gained weight throughout the process. Sometimes this is tolerable because you know that you can lose it once the patient is restored to health. But in other cases, extra weight gain for other family members (siblings, spouses, etc.) can be harmful to their own health. This is where you need to draw the line. Each person in the family must eat what is good for his or her OWN health. The ED patient may need to gain weight, but perhaps Mom and Dad do not. If they do gain weight, there is no need to panic — this just means you need to revisit the treatment plan and find a solution.

But always keep in mind that the patient is aware of what everyone else eats. You cannot send out the message that no one else eats cake in the family, but then insist that she eat cake. Be consistent. Remember that no food is bad food, and that everything in moderation is critical for healthy living. In my case, my family did not routinely use butter and oil in our foods. So, when my mom decided to give me a bagel with butter one morning, I was hysterical. I flat out refused, and I stared at the bagel for nearly two hours until she removed it. What do you do in this case? If your family does not use these ingredients, tell the patient that the solution is to eat foods in greater quantities. For example, a bagel without butter can be around 300 calories, whereas one with butter can be almost 450 calories. So, if she doesn't want the butter, she has to make up these calories by adding something else — a smoothie, a cup of whole milk, a dessert, etc. For me, this meant that I was eating enormous quantities of food because I refused to have any "added" fats in my meals. If this works for you, do it.

What you also need to remember is that while a patient will refuse to eat "extras" such as butter, oil, and desserts, she does need a certain amount of fat for proper digestion and assimilation. Indeed, in normal, healthy adults, fats should make up 20 to 35 percent of one's daily calories. We need fats for cushioning, protection, hormones, cell membranes, and more. It is not realistic to eliminate all fats from the patient's diet—she NEEDS them. If she doesn't want "butter," perhaps you can use a small quantity, but not excessive. If she gets too full after eating, maybe you can supplement her meals with a high-calorie smoothie or a drink like Boost or Ensure. Using supplementary drinks or shakes can be helpful for the patient because they add calories and nutrition without taking up a lot of room in her stomach. You can get creative with drinks by adding oil, cream, ice cream, chopped nuts, fruits, and more. Another benefit of these drinks is that when the patient has gained enough weight, it is relatively easy to eliminate the drinks from the menu without making her feel as though she can no longer eat freely.

The patient can also benefit from taking digestive enzyme supplements, which may or may not help relieve the stomach pain and speed stomach motility. One commonly prescribed medication is Motilium (domperidone), which is typically taken half an hour before meals. This medication is thought to speed stomach motility, which can help relieve the feeling of being very full after meals. There are many pills out there, so be careful. It is best to take the advice of a medical team before giving the patient any medications, even if it is an herbal supplement.

And there is one danger with supplements that you must always be aware of: excessive reliance on them can make the patient get used to them and in some cases replace her meals with them. For example, when my family told me that if I didn't eat, I would have to drink an Ensure, I rapidly agreed. And I drank it. I was angry, but this was better than eating! The issue here, though, was that this stopped me from learning that normal people do not drink all their calories; in fact, it is normal to eat and then drink. Without eating enough, the patient may not learn that normal eating requires her to EAT, not drink her meals. Again, your treatment team can help you find the approach that works for you.

All right, so now we have the patient eating. Who checks her weight? When does this happen? These are great questions, and I wish there were one easy answer. In terms of weighing, many caregivers do this at home, once a week in the morning, before eating but after voiding. Should the patient see her weight? Again, this is totally individual. Many treatment facilities state that the patient should see the weight so that she gets accustomed to the number. Weight is just a number, nothing else. It does not define how "good" the patient is, how successful she is, or how beautiful she is. It's like a shoe size: 6 . . . 7 . . . 10 . . . we need to know the number to make sure the patient is progressing, but it does not tell us whether or not she is a good human being.

Other teams, however, realize that seeing the number on the scale is distressing and can hinder progress. For example, a patient might see the weight gain and refuse to eat for the rest of the day, thereby slowing recovery. She may also refuse to eat whatever her caregivers are serving because of the weight gain, and she may state that she has lost trust in the caregivers. Once again, it seems as though we are in a lose-lose situation.

In my own experience, I saw my weekly weight gain and I saw the number on the scale. At first, my parents would weigh me and tell me whether I was up or down. But then, when I gained the weight back and saw the final number, I was distressed, angry, and became rebellious. Once I had gained it all back, I again fell down the hole and restricted, only to lose more weight than the first time. My parents realized that by showing me the weight gain each week, I would be angry at the moment, but in the long run, it would reinforce the fact that during recovery, weight gain is necessary and it would not mean much to me whether I weighed XXZ pounds or XXY pounds.

Actually, when I was in recovery during my first year of university, I found that weighing at home was too stressful for all of us. My parents and I agreed that I would be weighed at the dietitian's office, and they would hear back from her whether I had gained or lost. This seems to work for many parents because it removes the stress of weighing at home, and also gives accurate measurements.

You can arrange for the patient to be weighed every week at her medical team's location. Whether she sees the number or not depends on the age of the patient, your preference, and what your treatment team believes will be helpful. Remember that if she doesn't know her weight, a nurse or doctor might accidently mention her weight to her, and that would totally defeat the purpose of blind-weighing. So be careful and consistent in what you choose to do.

One last thing to keep in mind: The patient may try very hard to "fake" her weight gain. I have heard stories of water-loading (drinking a lot of water before weighing), sewing weights in undergarments, hiding rocks in shoes, etc. To avoid this, it might be necessary to weigh the patient in an undergarment or hospital gown, or to supervise her before the weigh-in. Some teams also do "random" weigh-ins so that the patient does not know when she will be weighed.

Your treatment team may also use the body mass index (BMI) charts to keep track of the patient's weight. What is BMI? It is calculated by dividing one's weight in kg by the height in meters squared. Generally, a value of 18.5–24.9 is normal, less than 18.5 is underweight, and more than 25 is overweight. Many treatment centres try to get patients to a BMI of around 20–23. However, keep in mind that while BMI can be a helpful tool, it is not perfect. Why? First of all, BMI does not take into account other factors, such as muscle mass. If a man with a lot of muscle calculates his BMI, he would likely be in the overweight section. But is he overweight? No. He simply has more muscle, which makes his weight higher. But this weight is muscle, not fat; thus, he might not truly be overweight. What about a child who genetically has bigger or thicker bones than "normal"? Her bones will be heavier, but is she fat? No. Her bones just weigh more; thus, her BMI may not be an accurate measure of her health. The problem with using BMI in ED patients is that a patient may have a normal BMI and still have an eating disorder. Moreover, even if a patient reaches a "normal BMI," she may still be ill and have eating-disordered thoughts. As a result, BMI is not the only measurement that should be used when determining what weight the patient should reach.

Other factors to keep in mind are mental and emotional well-being, blood tests, and ECG results, etc. Also, understand that once a patient reaches a healthy BMI, she is not "cured" of ED, and she still requires treatment and support. Recovery does not stop once she is weight-restored. Do not get caught up in the process of finding the "goal weight" for the patient, as this can change. Rather, a "weight range" should be determined, and the patient should ideally maintain a weight within that range. In addition, a patient who is still growing or will continue to grow would need this weight to be adjusted as she grows. Remember: Recovery is not a sprint, it is a marathon!

Now, let us assume that the first week has gone by and you are utterly exhausted. You took time off of work to stay with the patient while she eats, but how long can you do this? You cannot possibly take off a few months to feed the patient, can you? Who will bring in the money? And what about the patient—how will she learn if she isn't at school? Some people have found that their employers are understanding and permit them to take time off. Others cannot do this because of job limitations or because they need the income. This is often where caregivers start to feel pressured and stressed. Some have found that it was necessary for them to temporarily quit their jobs in order to restore the patient back to health.

Does it sound extreme? If you think so, try rephrasing the ED into cancer. What if your child had cancer, another life-threatening illness? What if she needed you to be home with her in order to take her medicine and recover? Many parents would not think twice about staying home in this case. Well, eating disorders are just as serious, just as deadly, and just as important. The patient may need someone to ensure that she is taking her medicine (i.e., food). If you cannot take time off, is it possible for you and your spouse or other caregivers to alternate shifts? Can your child come to work with you? Note that this is often not recommended, as a patient during the re-feeding process may be violent, angry, and emotionally unstable. Taking her to work with you may cause unneeded and unwanted attention, and it also does not tell the patient that her health is the most important issue at hand. Another option would be sending the patient to school, provided that she is monitored during mealtimes. Note that this will only work if she is medically, mentally, and emotionally able to go to school and learn. Can a teacher supervise meals? Can you come to school during lunch to eat with them? Some parents have found it helpful to send lunch to school with the child and have a teacher check the contents before lunchtime. The patient eats within sight of the teacher, and the teacher ensures that the lunch has been completed. This means that as a parent, you need to communicate with the teacher and let him know what you packed for lunch, as the patient may throw her food out before lunchtime. Again, this might not be realistic for all families because it is hard to find a reliable and willing teacher who can supervise the patient while eating. Some parents have found that it is easier and safer for the patient to stay at home during the re-feeding process.

But if the patient (or you, if you are the patient) stays at home, how will she learn and move onto the next grade with her peers? Some parents have found that their child is unable to go to school and focus on learning during recovery. In this case, you may find it helpful to keep in contact with teachers and get homework and assignments to do at home if possible. In other cases, she may not be able to do any work at all, and perhaps she will need to take a year off from school. A lot of parents and patients alike object to this because they do not want the patient to fall behind. However, if she is unable to perform well in school, it may be beneficial for her to focus on recovery now until she is actually able to do her work well. This is a hard decision to make, and the patient may feel sad and angry about this, but sometimes it is necessary. Many parents have found another solution to this issue, which is homeschooling or online schooling. This allows the patient to work at her own pace (usually) and learn, but she is still able to remain at home and eat, as well as be safe.

When I was ill, I absolutely refused to stay at home from school. School and learning play an important part in my life, and I was not prepared to give that up. In fact, learning is what motivated me to recover. In this case, my parents and I agreed that giving up school would hinder rather than help my progress. For the first while, I ate all my meals at home but ate lunch on my own at school. Note that this was because I had eaten many meals at home during the summer and was prepared to eat one meal on my own at school.

Some patients are ready for this, while others are not. Keep in mind that even if a patient is ready, the ED may become stronger at times and may push her to still throw out her food when she is alone. The scale will let you know if this is happening, and usually, the patient will confess to ditching her food. If this happens, remember: "*Feedback, not failure.*" It simply means that she is not yet ready to eat on her own. Don't be discouraged—just find a solution to the problem. Challenges occur frequently throughout the recovery process because it is not easy. Recovery is not a sprint, it is a marathon. What does that mean? It means that you should not rush into recovery, thinking that it will be over before you know it. Recovery takes a lot of time, effort, patience, and perseverance. It also means that there is no rush to make the patient eat on her own. If she is ready to, it is safer for her to eat with you. Of course, in the long run, she DOES need to learn to eat without supervision. But in the early stages, don't worry about this being a priority: just get the food in, and keep it in.

All right, you've come quite far. The patient is gaining weight and eating. But now it's your cousin's wedding and she expects the entire family to be there. How will the patient go? How will she eat enough? No one else knows about the eating disorder, and the patient doesn't want anyone to know. How do you deal with this? Some parents find that during the recovery process, some things need to go on hold. If possible, maybe it's best for you to skip this wedding and apologize for your absence. But what if you can't miss it? Try to see if it is feasible for only you to go, but the patient and the other caregiver(s) to stay home. If this still isn't possible, make a plan with the patient and inform her of what will happen. Perhaps at the buffet, you will make up her plate and sit with her while she eats.

What about the big family Christmas get-together? You know the one. When your own parents start talking about how much weight they have gained, and all your thin cousins give details about the latest diets they have been on. How in the world is the patient going to survive this one? My family and I found it helpful to educate others about the disorder. If possible, tell your family beforehand that there should be no talk of dieting, weight loss, food, etc., at the gathering. If they are willing to learn more, refer them to helpful resources or books. You may be surprised at how supportive your friends and family can be.

On the other hand, some people will simply not get it. I had a friend of mine stare at me when I told her I had ED. She replied, "So, why don't you just get your head on straight and eat? What is the big deal?" Clearly, she wasn't willing to learn about ED. What do you do then? I learned that these people, unfortunately, are more harmful than helpful. If they are not willing to educate themselves about ED, then they are not helping the situation. Some families have found that during festivities and occasions, it was necessary and safer for them to postpone gatherings until the patient got better. If this is possible and works for you, go for it.

However, you may feel that you and your family are now missing out on some special times. If you decide to attend, try to make a plan ahead of time. My parents and I phoned the hosts and asked what food would be served, explaining that one of us had a health issue and we needed to know what she could eat there. If we knew what was being served, my parents and I could make a plan for what I would eat there. Again, this isn't always possible. Sometimes, I actually did bring my own meals to parties. But no one said anything to me. Why? Because we educated the hosts before we arrived. In the event that someone did comment, we would reply that I had a health issue that required that I eat only certain foods and amounts. No one usually inquired further.

Always plan ahead for parties, outings, activities, and events. This will take a great deal of stress off of the patient and her friends/family when the day arrives. In this way, she can enjoy the gathering without worrying about the food, weight talk, triggering conversations, etc.

Whew! It's been a while since you have started re-feeding, and now the patient has reached her goal weight, or is almost there. What happens now? Does she eat on her own, choosing her own meals? Does her weight still have to be checked every week? Does she still need to gain weight because she is a growing child? First, remember that all growing bodies continue to grow until they are anywhere from twenty to twenty-five years old (or more, for some people). This is because bodies are preparing for adulthood and need energy. In a younger patient, even if her target weight has been reached, remember that as she grows taller, her weight must increase as well. A professional medical team can help with this. Just remember that for a young sufferer, the "target weight" will have to be adjusted many times as she grows, and that food is used for many different bodily functions.

Now, let's get back to the part about eating independently. How do you know when and if the patient is ready to do this? Some treatment facilities use a "staged" approach. In this model, stage one is re-feeding, which involves the caregivers feeding the patient. This is where the majority of weight gain happens. Stage two is when the caregivers work with the patient to give back some control over eating, such as meal planning, choosing dishes, eyeballing portions, etc. Stage three is when the treatment team, caregivers, and patients work on the other problems or issues in the patient's life, such as depression, OCD, anxiety, personal development, etc. Some parents find this approach to be helpful because it provides a rough outline of what is expected of them during treatment. However, many parents feel that it is easier to develop their own treatment plan that is tailored to their own needs. Again, this all depends on the patient and caregivers.

Most of the time, the patient cannot learn to eat independently right away, so she relies on the caregivers to feed her. It is only after a lot of work that insight into recovery and independence can be achieved. In this light, the "staged" approach does seem to be helpful. Keep in mind that each situation and every patient is different, so the timeline for each "stage" will also vary. Some families find that the patient regains the weight in three or four months, but it takes years before she can eat independently. Others find that weight gain is slow and steady, and throughout the process, the patient has learned to eat on her own. This is what happened in my case. I was very motivated to do whatever it took to recover, so I trained myself to eat on my own, and to eat enough. With the help of a dietitian, I learned to choose my own portions and meals. In this sense, my recovery did not fall into the "stages" that are set out by some treatment centres. But it worked for my family and me, and that is what matters.

Don't get too caught up and worried if the patient's recovery path is not like that of all other patients—just ensure that she is recovering and working toward a healthy life. *Recovery is not always a straight path, and there is more than one road to take.* As for weight checks, these can be helpful occasionally to ensure the patient is maintaining a healthy weight and eating enough. When she has maintained a healthy weight for a while, you and your team may decide that weight checks can be biweekly or less frequently.

How does the patient learn to take control over her eating and eat enough? More details on that appear in chapter six. For now, take a long, deep breath. You have just read through a great deal of information, covering everything from meals to checking weights. Before you put the book down for a stretch or a nutritious meal (is it dinnertime yet?), I want to leave you with some very important tips or key points to remember for caregivers and/or parents of a patient with ED. There is indeed a lot to know, and this process can be so overwhelming and stressful.

Important tips for caregivers

● Do not get angry in front of the suffering patient.
Or, more realistically, try to control your frustration and remember that it is not the patient, but ED talking and acting. I know that re-feeding a patient is extremely hard. I saw my

mother and father cry many times because I was unable to eat my meals, or because I screamed and said that I hated them. Oftentimes, it did not affect me because I was too entrenched in the ED. However, sometimes it hurt me because it made me feel that I was the cause of all the distress in my house. After a while, I told my parents that I needed them to be stronger than I was. I needed them to show ED that even if I was too tired or weak to fight, they would do it for me. They eventually learned that being angry or shouting at ED was not helpful; in fact, it made things worse.

If there is one thing my parents learned from this experience, it is definitely that parents HAVE to be strong. I understand that there will be many moments in which the ED will be loud and snarling in your face. You might hear your child say things that you have never heard before. It will break your heart to witness your child's inability to engage in a normal human activity—eating. It will make you cry that your child has to suffer day and night with a cruel voice that battles her at each and every meal. It stinks. You are a parent/caregiver and you have a right to worry about the patient. But the patient feels hurt and insecure when caregivers shout and scream. It makes her anxious and scared, and she often blames herself for everything. So, the best way to resolve this issue is to merely remain calm.

Some parents say that "Magic Plate" works best—when parents prepare the meals without the input of the patient, and then she is required to finish all of it. If she refuses to do this, parents are to remain calm and firmly but lovingly tell the child that ALL food must be eaten. As I mentioned before, you need to find the technique that works best for you and your family.

Whatever you do, remember that everyone eventually cracks under pressure. When dealing with the monstrous ED, you are bound to get angry, frustrated, and sad. If you break down one day, don't let it discourage you. That is a normal response for anyone fighting this battle. Just make sure that you have a safe and assertive way to express your emotions. Talking to a therapist, friend, or spouse can be relieving. Don't assume that having a therapist to talk to means that you are crazy and cannot handle your problems on your own! In fact, having a therapist—someone outside of the family circle who is not biased—can be very soothing. It provides you with a time and space to let out your feelings.

● Make life meaningful.
Life is tough, but when one is fighting an eating disorder, life is even harder! Food is the biggest fear of an anorexic; thus, being faced with food many times in one day is extremely terrifying. To combat this fear, my parents decided to make many distractions and activities in my life. For example, my mom began purchasing colourful tablecloths and flowers to decorate our dinner table with. At first, I didn't appreciate it at all. However, as I recovered, I began to enjoy the beautiful patterns on the various tablecloths. During re-feeding, different tablecloths and flowers in a vase helped to keep me distracted. Distractions are extremely important when re-feeding an anorexic patient. Other distractions that helped me included board games. I could not play games while eating (although some patients can), but the board games were useful after or before a meal. Whenever I was experiencing an ED thought, my parents instantly started a conversation with me. Of course, these were often meaningless and odd conversations (for example, "Can you believe how cold it is today!"), but they certainly kept me busy during the day . . . especially during meals.

Also, try keeping the patient involved in other interesting activities. My parents and I enjoyed purchasing books and sitting in our family room to read. Watching comedy films and shows also kept us entertained. At the beginning of re-feeding, I was unstable and could not take any walks anywhere. However, as I improved, my family and I took walks in the mall, around stores, and even around our own home!

Activities might be restricted at first, but as the patient gets better, you will have more options. Whatever you are doing, try your best to make it enjoyable for you, the patient, and other family members. Battling this illness is a very hard experience, and you may have many arguments and fights during the day (mostly focused on food, probably). But, at the end of the day, you must realize that every morsel of food that went in and stayed in the patient brings you one step closer to their recovery. Every challenge won against ED is progress. The patient may or may not be thankful for your efforts — but don't let that stop you. When the feeding is over, try to enjoy life.

This disorder, while tough, brought my family closer. Despite all the yelling and screaming that went on during this process, we learned to appreciate one another. We learned that being healthy and alive together is a gift and a blessing. We learned that spending time together, playing games, or watching movies is time well spent. *Each day that goes by is one day closer to recovery and health.* Make the most of it.

🍎 Do not give up and never stop fighting.

Mistakes and challenges will happen. There will be many times in which you feel frustrated, angry, hopeless, and heartbroken. Re-feeding is definitely a difficult task for anyone to take on, as it involves a tremendous amount of time, patience, love, dedication, and effort. Recall that helping a loved one toward recovery does not only mean feeding her; it also means staying with her before and after meals to sooth her anxiety, listening to her fears around food and weight, and ensuring that she is as relaxed as can be.

Early on in re-feeding, I was depressed, sad, and angry. I was rude to my parents whenever they tried to feed me, and my moods changed within a matter of seconds. I said things to my parents that I have never said before, including words that must have torn their hearts to pieces. But they never gave up. When I asked my parents (after I recovered) how they managed to remain so strong and vigilant all the time, they responded: "We are your parents. We love you and care for you . . . way too much to have let ED take our baby girl away from us. If you were having a hard time, we knew that ED was trying to gain power over you. *Even though those were the hardest times to remain calm and strong, we knew that we had to be your strength. If ED thought that he was fighting you alone, we had to show him that you had a fierce and persevering army right behind you."*

Remind yourself of this daily and whenever you feel defeated. Don't expect each day to be easy. Indeed, the patient may eat co-operatively one day but be completely resistant the next. One week may show a one-pound gain, and the next may show no gain at all. Do not be discouraged. Re-feeding and recovery is a bumpy road, and it is not always as easy as pie (Lemon meringue? Apple? I'll let you choose!). If something does not go as planned, don't let it deter you. This is easier said than done.

But always remember that each time something does go wrong, you can learn from it. Did the patient just throw her breakfast on the floor and refuse to eat? Did she threaten to run away from home because she hates you? Did her weight not improve even though you have been feeding her consistently? Don't panic—just learn, plan, and move on. Maybe ED is louder today, and the patient is having a hard time eating. Perhaps more distractions would be useful. Or perhaps her weight has not moved because her metabolism has sped up and now she needs more food. Maybe it's just a bad day and ED is not going to be that lenient today.

Whatever the cause of the problem, you need to be like a group of Boy Scouts: always prepared. Anticipate that somewhere along the way, things will get tough. In fact, it is not uncommon for caregivers to see increased resistance as the patient recovers. This is often called an "extinction burst" or the "last ten pounds." The patient can suddenly get resistant, especially now that she is stronger and nourished. She might refuse to eat meals and might even become violent. If this happens, you may just be hitting a sour spot (don't you love those sour candies?) that ED doesn't want you to reach. Do not be dismayed and don't give up. Just keep going and keep feeding. It often gets worse right before it starts to get better. In any case, make sure that you and the patient are safe.

🍎 Make time for yourself and spend time "away from the eating disorder."

I realize that this is hard—after all, if re-feeding is a full-time job, how can there be any time for you? Most often, people will suggest taking a break by enlisting the help of a trustworthy friend or family member. If you believe that your child will not be able to eat with these adults due to major resistance, then perhaps you can ask someone to come help you clean your home. Friends can also pick up and babysit other children of yours, go grocery shopping, or even cook meals for you. If you are a married couple, make sure that you sit with one another every so often to discuss things other than your ill child, such as your goals, how your day went, interesting stories, etc.

If, for any reason, you decide to take time off of work, remember not to regret this; your child is ill and enslaved by a horrible and LIFE-THREATENING disease. As a parent, YOU KNOW THAT YOUR CHILD NEEDS YOU THE MOST. Work and money can wait. Your child's schooling, if need be, can also wait. Only after your child is fully recovered can she take on life's challenges, including education, occupations, etc. Set priorities: the number one thing that must be done is to free your child from ED's grip.

Nevertheless, it is absolutely essential for you to take time off from this difficult journey. Try to find time for yourself—you can book a massage, see a therapist, go out for coffee with a friend, have a dinner date with your spouse, or even read a good book in the bathtub. It may seem impossible to do this, and sometimes it is not feasible (especially in the early re-feeding days). Over time, as the patient progresses, try to think of things that can be done to make yourself relaxed or happy. For example, if the patient has just eaten a meal and is sleeping, that can be your time to paint your nails or watch a sports game. If you can ask your family to come help, maybe they can keep the patient occupied in a game while you make phone calls or chat with friends. I guarantee that your experiences with ED will make you realize that even the simplest things in life can be pleasurable and enjoyable.

If you are in a marriage or partnership, remember that this needs attention as well. So do your other children, if applicable. Even the patient needs attention for things other than eating! Once meals are over, think of what you can do for yourself. As I've said before, even watching a movie as a family can be a very rewarding and relaxing experience. If you have decided to spend time alone with your partner, try to make time to discuss things other than ED. Talk about the other things in your life. The same applies when spending time with the patient. Remember that she is so much more than ED—she has feelings, dreams, goals, and hobbies. In the day or week, allot some time for activities when ED is not invited.

❦ Educate yourself and others around you.
There are so many factors that play into eating disorders. In fact, each case may be unique with respect to the sufferer, his/her conditions/diagnosis, and the family's situation. That being said, it is impossible to generalize information regarding what techniques work best, how fast recovery will occur, etc. The solution? Find out as much as you can. Helpful individuals might include a therapist, a dietitian, a family doctor, etc. There are also many reliable resources that can provide you or others with information about ED. The more you learn, the more you will understand how to deal with ED, and this will help prepare you for future battles (like dinner wars, for example). Gaining insight into what the recovery experience is like for the patient can be very useful because it allows you to see things through the patient's eyes.

Referring your friends and family to resources is also beneficial because they can learn how they can be of assistance to you. Learning never stops. You may even find it beneficial to meet or talk with other parents who have children with ED and are also in the same trenches. This can be a great source of support and advice for you (but keep in mind that everyone's case is different). Don't forget to ask questions of the treatment team. Be informed of what is going on, what the goals are, how you are progressing.

And last of all, *take time to appreciate how far you have come.* Take the time to reflect on the day or week and see how many battles you have won against ED. Of course, ED will win sometimes. That is normal. What is important is that you keep fighting and learn from every experience. My parents have told me time and time again that even on the hardest days of recovery, they would remember the food that was nourishing my body and, despite how many times I refused to eat or yelled, they would feel satisfied in knowing that I was one step closer to health. I guarantee that if there is one thing you will learn from this entire experience, it is to persevere and remain strong. You will learn to take joy in even the simplest things, such as the sun shining, hearing the patient sing a song, listening to relaxing music, or seeing her grow stronger and healthier. Count your blessings each day. It will make you appreciate life to the fullest.

Each day might not be a good day, but there is a little good in each day.

ED can really test your patience. Do not let him win any battles. If he does, do not worry. He may win some small battles, but you will win the final war.

Chapter Six

Give ED a pizza your mind

After feeding and feeding, the patient has finally reached her goal weight and has stabilized. Just when you thought the work was over, your treatment team remembers one more thing: The patient now needs to learn how to eat on her own. She needs to learn how to choose what to eat, when to eat, and how much. Surely it cannot be that difficult! She has been eating for months, now! How hard can it be?

First, let us revisit the dreaded scale for a moment. How do you actually know when the patient is maintaining? As she ventures toward eating independently, surely her weight must be monitored. But how do you know if her weight is again tumbling down? Is one pound down or one pound up a bad sign when she is supposed to be maintaining? The simple answer is that we need to focus on the *pattern* of weight gain or loss. Typically, medical teams ask that patients gain two to five pounds more as an extra cushion. This way, if she happens to lose weight during the quest for independence, she is not in a dangerous place. The bottom line is that trends in weight are usually more important than weekly values. Consistent weight loss is an alarming sign. Consistent weight gain may be appropriate if the patient is growing. A stable weight is reassuring if the patient has not grown nor needs any extra energy. Remember, too, that weight will fluctuate in certain cases—for example, a female might gain a few extra pounds prior to menstruating. Or the patient might gain weight if she is building muscle mass. Again, focus on the overall trend, and don't be shy about bringing to the treatment team any questions or concerns you have.

Let me warn you: it's hard. This task is not an easy egg to crack (Omelet? Sunny side up?). Helping the patient to eat on her own means that you are training her to eat what is necessary for her to stay healthy. It means giving up some control over the feeding process and letting her make some decisions. To be honest, it is a bit daunting. It is hard to decide how much control should be handed over, what the patient should have a say in, and how often this should occur. One thing to remember is that a patient might not be ready for this, even when her weight has stabilized and she is healthy. In fact, some caregivers find that patients still need to be monitored and cannot eat independently for months.

However, the patient cannot remain dependent on you for too long. She needs to gradually learn how to feed herself. How this occurs is different for each patient, and your team may be able to help you decide what is best for you. This chapter will focus on some ways or tips to help you train the patient to maintain some level of independence. Note that even when one technique works, it might not be reasonable to expect the patient to do it every day. For example, she can portion her plate one day, but you might not have her do this every single day. Work in baby steps so that she does not get overwhelmed, but still makes progress.

You can start the process by casually having the patient eat a meal while you do something else. For example, instead of staying by her side at the table, get up and do something in the same room, such as washing dishes. Explain that you know that she is now able to eat without your watching every bite. This way, if ED decides to make her throw food away, you will be able to spot it. Be mindful that ED might make her chew and spit food into napkins or pockets, or under the table onto the floor. ED may make her even throw food to the pet. This is why you start by remaining in the same room, but not at the table: you can catch ED in the act. Before she leaves the table, you may have to check her pockets. Make sure her mouth is empty; ED may make her put food in her mouth, only to spit it out once you are gone. If all goes well, hooray! You can try this several times, and next time, perhaps you can even step out of the room for a while. If the patient struggles, it is okay. This just means that she needs a little more training, confidence, and help. Empowering the patient is also helpful. Tell her that you know that she is stronger than ED and is able to eat. Let her know that you are proud of how far she has come, and that you think it is time for her to try to eat without your being by her side.

What comes next? You can try moving forward a bit now. Perhaps the next step will be allowing the patient to plate her own food. Give her a spoon and tell her to put enough rice on a plate. The great thing about this is that you are right there beside her. If she puts enough, you can give the okay and let her sit and eat. If there isn't enough, kindly suggest that she add more. What if there's too much? This doesn't happen very often, because patients usually have portion distortion (more on that in chapter nine). However, if it does, gently tell the patient to remove some from the plate. Picking portion sizes can be very hard and distressing for the patient because she wants to do it "just right" and doesn't want to eat more than she has to. Reassure her that you will not let her eat too much or too little. That is why you are right there with her.

If all goes well, continue doing this for the next few days. Maybe next time, the patient can plate her own cereal, pour her own juice, or choose her preferred pizza slice. Practice makes perfect! Don't be dismayed if one day she plates enough, but the next day she plates too little. ED might be playing the guilt trick and making her feel bad for "willingly eating." Be there to comfort and coach her. Let her know that you are confident in her ability to estimate portions.

Evidence shows that people with ED (specifically anorexia) are more likely to overestimate the sizes of meals. This means that the patient may have difficulty in learning how much is "enough" when it comes to eating, and this can take a long time to master. Do not rush if the patient is not ready—she will get there someday. Be patient and do your best to help her learn how to feed herself. This is an essential skill if she is to maintain a healthy weight in the future.

When can the patient choose her own meals? Now might be a good time to spice things up a bit (parsley or garlic?). Pay attention, here, because this can get tricky: The patient may have extreme anxiety over choosing what to eat, and she may become violent, angry, tearful, or terrified. It is best to take it in steps. A good way to start is by giving the patient simple options. For example, would she prefer a chocolate or strawberry smoothie? Does she want cheese or creamy sauce on her pasta? Does she prefer to have a muffin or a bagel for breakfast? Keep in mind that when giving these options, the foods offered should be nutritionally equivalent. What does this mean? They should provide roughly the same amount of calories. This way, the patient does not get caught up in trying to choose the lower calorie option each time. Also, limit it to one of two options, because more than this can overwhelm the patient. And don't forget to stress that she *must* pick one of the things you just stated. Negotiating for a third option is not on the menu. It is either "a" or "b," not "c." Reassure her that whatever she chooses, the nutrition is the same (if that is something she is concerned with).

Often, she will not want to make these choices, because ED does not want her to ever choose to eat. You can handle this by telling the patient that she has to eat one of the two options, so she should choose something she wants to try or prefers. If this is still too hard, ask which food she prefers the smell or colour of. If this still doesn't work, make one option today and give the other option tomorrow.

Choosing what to eat, even when given only two options, is very stressful for many patients. I cried the first time my mom told me to choose between a chocolate brownie and a vanilla muffin. It was too hard! ED was filling my head with thoughts on which had fewer calories. ED was calling me useless and fat for actually choosing something that I wanted to eat. I told my mom that I could not choose. She made me close my eyes and pick "one or two." She had written each option on a piece of paper, and whatever matched with the number I chose was what I ate. As time progressed, I was able to choose what I wanted to eat.

Hunger cues may also be blunted in anorexic patients for a long time, making it even harder to decide what to eat. This is an adaptive response by the starving body: The brain blunts hunger feelings in order to make the patient survive despite food restriction. This means that as the patient recovers, she may need guidance and assistance in choosing what to eat, as well as when she should eat. Using a guideline, such as eating every three to four hours, can be a useful way to deal with this.

Let's assume that all of this has worked so far, and you have done it enough times so that the patient can choose one of two options and eat while you are doing something else away from the table. Perhaps the next step is to let her eat a meal away from you. This can be done by sending her with food to a friend's house or to her sibling's room. Make sure, however, that wherever she is eating, someone is supervising her and checks that she has eaten (and not ditched) her meals. If this seems difficult, you can let her eat in the kitchen while you go make a phone call. Remember that this is a big step because you are trusting the patient to eat on her own, and you might not see where every bite lands. This step takes a lot of time to reach. After the patient is done, search around the place. Did she hide any food anywhere?

If in doubt, the next weigh-in can let you know whether or not she has been eating her meals when you are not around. If her weight falls, you should ask her straight up what happened. She might lie, but eventually, she will give in and admit hiding food, especially if you state that now she needs to eat more because her weight went down because she hasn't been eating enough. If this happens, don't give up. This just means that she needs more practice. If all goes well, you can move on to the next step: having the patient eat an entire meal on her own at school (or work, wherever) without anyone at all watching.

You've come so far, and now you believe that the patient is ready to eat out. This is a major challenge for her because she has become used to the safety of eating at home. In addition, she may not be comfortable eating in front of people other than those who are usually at home. What's more, eating out can be difficult for her because the food is not prepared at home; thus, she may be anxious about the calorie content or use of butter, oil, etc. Portions can also be hard to estimate in restaurants because they are usually larger than usual.

A first step might be ordering restaurant food for delivery or takeout. This way, the patient can eat "fast food," but still be in a safe environment. This is also a good idea in the early days because the patient might be anxious and can get loud, which can be a tad embarrassing and difficult to deal with when in public.

Let's assume that you've done this already and are now prepared to actually sit in a restaurant or fast-food joint to eat. First, what should she order—and do you choose her food? If you think she is ready to choose her own meal, discuss it with her and agree before she orders. If not, perhaps you can make the decision at first, as the experience can already be anxiety-provoking for the patient. Now, what do you do about the portion sizes? If it is large, tell the patient that she needs to eat enough, but having leftovers is acceptable ONLY if she has eaten enough. As the caregiver, use your judgment to determine what "enough" is.

I will caution you on one thing: It may be better for the patient to eat first than for you to "pre-portion" how much she should eat. The problem with predetermining portions is that the patient might try to push food over onto the "uneaten" side, as if to pretend that she has already eaten what she needs to. On the flip side, she may keep asking, "Okay, is that enough?" if you do not do this, but rather simply instruct her to simply start eating until you say that she has eaten enough.

One helpful tip: Decide how much she needs to eat, and put the rest in a "to go" box. This way, you are demonstrating how much she needs to eat, and there can be no tricks. Of course, some may argue that this is not realistic because in the real world, no one divides meals into "to be eaten" and "not to be eaten" piles from the beginning. Again, you need to find out what works best for you. As time progresses, you will start to see that each new experience becomes easier for the patient, and she is able to become more independent. You may also start to feel the tension decrease as meals are eaten—before, during, or even after the patient has eaten. Remember that the goal right now is to assist her in developing normal eating habits. This means eating enough, eating a variety of foods, and being able to eat socially without a fuss.

Depending on the age of the patient, it might be necessary to help her grocery shop or prepare simple meals for herself. For example, preteens, teens, and young adults need these skills. This is hard to achieve because many individuals this age have no interest or desire to cook. But, in my case, I was heading into university. Although I would live at home, there would be times when I would be at home alone. What if Mom had not prepared my meals for me? It would be abnormal for me to sit in the house feeling hungry, waiting for her to come home. A normal person would find something to eat or purchase something from outside.

As I got better, I was able to visit grocery stores with my parents and purchase food items. I learned how to make simple dishes, snacks, and sandwiches that I could eat. Note that this is hard for the patient because now you are not only asking her to eat, but also to prepare a healthy and nutritious meal for herself. Going to grocery stores is also a challenge because she may feel anxious with all the food around her, or she might try to purchase only the lowest-calorie options. This is why this is often one of the last steps to take when building independence. For younger children, this step would likely not be necessary right away. However, for all patients, learning to get food independently when needed is important. The patient can practise by making her own breakfast under your supervision one morning, or helping you prepare her lunch. Over time, she will grow accustomed to preparing simple dishes or snacks, and she will learn how much food is a sufficient amount.

The path to independence is challenging. ED can rear his terrible head yet again and try to prevent the patient from eating or progressing. By now, caregivers might feel exhausted and just wish that everything were over. The good news is that by working toward independence, you are helping the patient work toward building a solid foundation for her life. You are teaching her to eat what her body needs, regardless of whether or not anyone is present to watch her eat. When I was recovering, something helpful for me to think about was, *If no one were at home and watching me, would I be eating this now?*

At the beginning, I would not have touched a single crumb of food if no one was at home. Indeed, I would not have eaten all day if I was left alone. However, as time progressed, I started to see and feel how much stronger I was when I ate. I noticed that eating helped me concentrate and achieve all my goals. My body was heavier, but it was also stronger and beautiful. In short, I needed to eat, even if no one was there to make sure that I did. After a while in recovery, I asked myself the same question. And this time, my answer was, *yes, I would eat.* It took time, but it did happen. This is why I still eat by the clock: I don't feel hungry, and without anyone with me, I might forget to eat, because my stomach and brain don't feel the need to seek out food.

Many patients experience this blunted response to food intake, and it might have something to do with the hunger hormone leptin. High amounts of leptin suppress appetite; low levels stimulate food intake. It seems that patients with ED have elevated leptin levels all the time, so they don't feel hungry even when they haven't eaten for a while.

Finally, the patient has gained enough weight and is maintaining, and she can even eat independently. As you celebrate and do a happy dance, you suddenly remember one more thing: There were other issues that came along or were present before ED. You know: the obsessive-compulsive disorder (OCD), depression, anxiety, trauma, perfectionism, mood instability, isolation, and so on. Sometimes it is hard to determine whether or not these conditions were present before ED, because ED makes everything seem a lot worse. Some patients have preexisting OCD and anxiety before ED took hold, but ED exaggerated them. Others may have depression as a result of ED.

Whatever the issues are, they now need to be addressed. Don't get me wrong—they were always important. But during the re-feeding phase, weight stabilization and health are top priorities. Now that the patient is healthy, you can direct your energy and time into working on the other things. Therapists can be supportive here—for you and/or the patient. In some cases, medication may be necessary. Many parents have noticed that their daughter seems to have somewhat of an OCD during ED. She may have certain rituals such as always eating from certain plates, chewing a certain number of times, washing her hands excessively, etc. She may have phobias around dirt, food locations, tests, or social gatherings. She may even have panic attacks or become extremely anxious. She can also suffer from depression because ED robs her of all happiness. ED usually numbs the patient's feelings and makes her cold to everything around her. ED also makes the patient not enjoy anything—food, funny movies, activities previously enjoyed, and more.

Different conditions require different treatments. For example, systemic desensitization is useful for phobias or OCD. An example of this would be if the patient is afraid to leave the house and begins to have a panic attack. You can expose her ever so slowly to varying degrees of the feared stimulus until she no longer fears it. In this case, you might start off by having her simply stand outside the door for a few minutes. In a week, you might walk with her to the park. After another few weeks, you can sit with her in a library.

For OCD, parents have found that stopping the ritual is difficult, but eventually, patients can overcome it. For example, a patient may feel compelled to always wrap her hands around her wrists as a measure of body checking. Whenever you see her do this, remind her not to do so. If the child is young, using a reward system ("Whenever you don't do XXX, you will get ZZZ as a prize") can be really helpful. Overcoming anxiety and depression, as well as insomnia, is also challenging. Anxiety and depression can be treated by seeing a therapist or participating in treatments such as DBT (dialectical behavioural therapy) or CBT (cognitive behavioural therapy). The great thing about DBT and CBT is that they teach the patient to control her thoughts, which will help control her feelings and actions. CBT is actually one of my favourite therapies because it helps the patient see how her thoughts affect her moods. By learning the connection between the two, she can start to see how she can change her thoughts ("I am a lazy and useless person") into something more appropriate and realistic ("I am not a lazy person just because I feel tired. I am not useless—I help around the house"). This, in turn, affects her moods because she starts to realize that by thinking good thoughts, she will feel good feelings. Chapter thirteen will go into a bit more detail about CBT. For insomnia, creating a calm and quiet environment for sleep can promote relaxation, and so can taking a warm bath before bed. Drinking milk has also been shown to promote sleep due to the tryptophan content.

Some caregivers have found that using medications has been very helpful for patients. For example, patients may have extreme anxiety during recovery. This anxiety is not your everyday worry—it is much more. Someone with an anxiety disorder gets extremely nervous and worked up over what appears to be trivial to others. She has full-blown panic attacks, such as hyperventilating, sweating, heart palpitations, etc. But, in some cases, anxiety can manifest itself through other symptoms, such as simply being really worried about something. I personally had extreme anxiety around food and weight. ED also filled my head with thoughts of failure, hopelessness, and fear. At times, I was so anxious that I could not eat. This is common in patients with ED. In some cases, medications can help, such as atypical neuropeptides (non-addictive but slow-acting medications) or benzodiazepines (fast-acting but addictive medications).

Using relaxation techniques such as deep breathing and meditation can also be useful. Patients may also struggle with depression, which is characterized by feelings of sadness and hopelessness. Depression is a common co-morbid condition in ED. Again, there are many types of medications for depression, including selective serotonin reuptake inhibitors (SSRIs), and other antidepressants. SSRIs are non-addictive, so it is not very difficult to wean patients off them. I used two different SSRIs to help with my depression and sleep troubles. Do not be ashamed of using medications in the treatment of ED, as sometimes medications can really help. At the same time, not all patients require medications. A medical team can help you determine if medications are needed for anxiety and/or depression.

Do note that the medical team should always be aware of any medications that patients are taking, and medications should be taken only for their intended purpose. The problem that can occur with medications is that they may cause dependence, and tapering down doses can be challenging due to withdrawal effects. This is why having a strong and informed medical team is helpful—they can let you know the benefits and side effects of any medications that can be prescribed. It is important to reinforce to the patient that if she needs medications, this does not make her "abnormal" or "crazy." We all take medications when we realize that they may help us, and this may or may not be for one's entire life. Regardless, medications are not bad; they can actually be quite beneficial in some cases. I have known many ED patients who have taken anti-depressants, and their moods have improved tremendously.

One final note about medications: caregivers may need them as well! This whole process is challenging not only for patients, but for care-givers, too. It is not wrong for you to feel exhausted, tired, depressed, or anxious during this journey. If you feel that you may need medication, talk to your doctor about it. Medications can help, even if they are taken temporarily. When you are fighting against a strong illness like ED, be open to trying interventions that may make things easier—whether this is meditation, medication, or both!

Chapter Seven

Use real butter,
there's no margarine for error

We've covered the basics of eating disorders—what they are, the dangers, and the "stages" or steps involved in re-feeding. But we have not yet covered HOW you actually make meals, how you encourage a patient to eat, and how to deal with the weight gain. This chapter will be particularly useful if you are a patient trying to recover, or if you are a caregiver trying to help someone recover.

A book about ED would simply not be complete without tips on how to prepare meals. But this is not a cookbook, and I am not a great chef. Nonetheless, in my experiences with recovery, I have seen that having some guidance about meal preparation is helpful. First, what kind of meals do you prepare? How many times should patients eat per day, and how often? Chapter five went into some details about how you can make nutritious meals that don't make the patient feel too full. But when do you serve up these meals? Normally, we all need to eat around every three to four hours. This keeps our bodies fuelled and ensures that we don't get too hungry in between meals. For someone without ED, this is relatively simple because you can grab something to eat when you feel the need to. However, remember that a patient with ED cannot do this—for many reasons. The most obvious one is that ED has taken control over her and prevents her from eating. This is an important message for all patients with ED, caregivers, and treatment providers to understand: A patient with ED cannot choose to eat; she is being controlled by this monstrous illness. If you tell her to eat, she will usually say that she "can't." What does this imply? It is not her will to eat or not. The illness is commanding her not to eat, and she feels obligated to obey. When I was ill, I could not even stand the sight of food prepared for me to eat. I yelled and shouted that I could not eat — that it was too hard and frightening. Many patients say that they feel the same way when asked to eat.

Now comes one of the most common questions: How do you make someone with ED eat? And if you are a sufferer, how do you sum up the courage to take a bite into recovery?

Always remember this: *It is ED that doesn't want you (or the patient) to eat. It is ED that fills the patient's head with commands that forbid food intake. It is ED that makes a patient feel guilty, fat, and useless if she "gives in" and eats.*

Knowing this will help you realize why it is such a challenge to eat with ED. The patient really would like to eat — she has been starving for way too long. But the sight of food makes her anxious because ED has such a strong hold over her and won't let her eat. She would eat if she could — she is hungry! But she CANNOT because ED has the upper hand. If you are a patient or a caregiver, it is time that to take things back into your hands. You must be clear that you refuse to step back and watch as ED continually robs the patient of her health, happiness, and life. You will not watch the patient be controlled by the monstrous beast. If you are a caregiver, telling the patient this takes a great deal of bravery. She will not be pleased when you lay down the law that you are feeding her and that she must eat. Inside, she may feel grateful that someone is MAKING her eat — this tends to be easier for the patient because she can "blame" her eating on you. It is as though she is telling ED that she is not making the choice to eat — you are commanding her to do so.

The patient may even question if she "has to eat." Once told that she does, she may grumble and fuss, but inside, this is relieving for her. At other times, she might flat out refuse to eat. She can throw plates on the floor, scream, say hateful things, and even become physically violent. If this happens, remember that what you are seeing is not the patient, but a manifestation of ED. This usually occurs when you have done something that ED hates, such as telling the patient to eat or helping her gain weight. At times like this, it can be very hard for caregivers to muster up enough bravery to keep fighting ED. You may be saddened that your loving and precious child is acting out at you in this way. But if you always remind yourself that this is the hideous beast that is slowly killing your child, you will be able to summon up the confidence needed to take charge.

One more thing about confidence—you can always fake it. As a caregiver, you might not feel strong or confident. You might not know that the patient will listen and eat. You may be terrified at the way your beloved child is acting now. *But you must act and appear to be confident and lovingly firm.* The patient needs to see this because it tells ED that Mom/Dad/caregivers are now in control.

Here are a few suggestions as to what you can say to a patient when she has to eat, is struggling to complete meals, or feels awful for "defying" ED:

● I love you too much to let this monster (ED) kill you. I know it is hard for you to eat, especially when ED is telling you not to. But I am your parent and I am telling you that you have to eat.

● It must be hard for you to do this, and I know that ED doesn't like it. I will sit with you as you eat and help you. Let's start by taking one bite. It will get easier.

● I'm not going to speak to ED right now. He is horrible and wants to take away my child from me. I understand that it is hard for you to ignore him, so I will help you.

● Until you eat, you cannot do anything else. If you are too sick to eat, then you cannot be well enough to do other things. As soon you as finish all of your meal, we can do XXX.

● This is what you need to be well. I will not give you more or less than what you need for health. I am not trying to make you fat; I am trying to save your life from ED.

● ED has taken control over you and wants to make you believe that you are fat, ugly, and a failure. But I will not let ED win. I will keep fighting until we defeat ED.

- Eating must be very hard for you, and I appreciate that. But you need food to stay alive. Right now, this is your medicine. It will help you get better. This is what you need.

- No one except ED is trying to ruin your life. ED is trying to kill you, but he is trying to convince you otherwise. I will not watch as ED takes you away from me.

- I want you to become better so that you can fulfill all of your dreams. But unless you eat and get healthy again, you cannot do this. ED is trying to sabotage your life by telling you not to eat.

- I will not discuss your weight or food with you. That is what the team is for. Your job is also not to worry about these things. All you have to do is eat. We will take care of everything else. The sooner you eat, the faster you will get better.

- I'm not stopping you from doing anything—it is ED. I am telling you that if you eat, you can do XXX. It is ED who is preventing you from having fun because he won't let you eat.

Now, what if the patient hates this kind of talk about ED? What if she insists that it is not ED that doesn't want to eat, but her? What if she screams for you to "shut up" and stop talking to her? This is always difficult, but it does happen. I personally hated it when my parents used to make the above statements. I felt that it was ME who did not want to eat. It was ME who was refusing my food. And besides, how could they stop me from doing anything?

You may have to deal with similar situations when helping a patient recover. Sometimes, it is best not to say anything at all. It is not rude to ignore ED and say nothing—but bear in mind that this could agitate patients as well. Sometimes it is best to hum or tune out ED. Will the patient like this? Probably not. But it can reinforce the fact that eating is not an option and not up for discussion. This is her food, and if she can eat the entire meal, her life gets to move on.

It seems a bit daunting that whatever you say or do, ED will be angry and make the patient act out. This is why you must ensure that the patient gets better by eating, gaining weight, and recovering. As long as the patient is malnourished, she will not be able to see how ED is ruining her life or controlling her.

What if you are a patient and want to help yourself eat? How can you do this? Chapter nine has a lot more information about this.

A helpful exercise for patients to complete is to create a list of pros and cons about living with ED. This can be done individually in order to allow the patient to express her true feelings. This is an extremely useful exercise because it can help you (or the patient) see how much ED has ruined life. Below is my own list of pros and cons.

Having ED in my life

Pros	Cons
I get to lose weight and be thin.	I am too thin and now feel weak and tired.
I can wear small-sized clothes, and people notice how thin I am.	I cannot get the courage to eat and I feel hungry all the time. I wish I could eat, but I can't.
No one calls me fat and ugly anymore.	I may be thin, but this hasn't solved all of my life's problems.
I can control my body and weight.	I miss out on fun times like birthdays and occasions because I cannot eat.

When I looked at this list, I realized that the "pros" were not really important or helpful. The "cons," on the other hand, had significant implications for my life. Try using this exercise with the patient. After she completes her list, discuss what she has written and what it means to her. Are the "pros" really good things? Do the "cons" outweigh the "pros"? If you are the patient, you may find it helpful to read this list over with someone you trust, such as a family member, friend, therapist, or pastor.

Patients cannot recover alone. Normally, people can sense when they need to eat. This doesn't typically occur in a patient with ED because her hunger cues have been suppressed for so long. This is why patients need to eat on a regular, timed schedule. If you are a patient, this may seem tedious at first, and it may even feel as though you are an automatic machine that is robotically eating. This is perfectly normal. As time progresses and you get better, you will become accustomed to eating. Right now, this may seem far off and like a distant dream. But I am living proof that this does happen.

When should meals be and how long should they be? It all depends, and a treatment team can be very helpful with this. In my case, I ate (and still do eat) at regular intervals. This is important because it maintains your blood sugar levels and ensures that the body has enough energy for all its needs. Remember that recovering from ED means that patients are not only eating for energy, but also to fix all the damage that ED has done to the body. This makes it even more important for her to eat regularly and enough.

A typical day for me is breakfast at 8:30, lunch at 12:30, snack at 3:30, dinner at 6:30, and another snack at 9:30 before bed. Basically, I eat every three to four hours. This is very important! Planning ahead is critical because it means that you do not need to make any last-minute decisions.

When I was ill, I realized that if I did not have food with me, I did not have the ability to go buy some. If the food wasn't there, I simply would not eat. This is why I packed all my food with me—it ensured that I wouldn't miss any meals. If I had a full day at school, I packed every single meal with me. If I thought I might be late, I still packed my food just in case. Did this mean that I had a lot of food with me on most days? Yes, it did. But focusing on one meal at a time was extremely help-ful. My lunch bag might be full now, but it has my entire day of meals in it. Now it is 12:30, and I am only eating lunch, not the entire day's meals. So now I will breathe, take out my lunch, and eat.

Another helpful tip is to set limits on mealtimes. A patient may tend to take very long to eat because she is nervous and is struggling to eat. Try to make each meal take a maximum of thirty minutes and snacks about fifteen minutes. Remember not to eat too fast, either. The patient might stuff her mouth with food to "get it over with." But recall that the goal of recovery is also to eat normally. Normal people do not stuff food in their mouths to simply complete the meal. They take reasonable (not too big or too small) bites, chew, and swallow. And then they repeat this until the meal is done.

At first, I found it helpful to eat with my family. We sat down and ate breakfast together. This was nice because it took my mind off of eating. I would also try to distract myself by reading, playing on my phone, or talking to my sister. Distractions can be your best friend during mealtimes because it relieves the distress of eating. Until today, I still use distractions during meals because it helps me stay relaxed and calm. The nice thing about having others around when you eat is that they can support you — but only if they understand eating disorders and can offer you encouragement. If someone you know will not be helpful, then don't sit with her while eating. This can hinder your progress.

Remember, too, that in the early days, your eating will be what is called "*mechanical eating*." You may feel like a robot as you check the time, see that it's time for a snack, take out your food, and start eating. It may feel "unnatural" to take bites and swallow your food. It may even feel painful and like a struggle. But that is normal. You have not eaten for so long because ED has made you starve. Expect resistance, even from yourself. But always know that this gets better, and that eating will truly become easier as you get used to it.

Before, I would get so nervous when I ate. After I ate would also be difficult. I would feel full, and ED would tell me that I just gained five pounds from that one meal. It was awful. This is why distractions and supportive people can also be helpful. This can take your mind off the distress. This is what is called "*distress tolerance*." It is ever so hard to eat meals, feel full, and gain weight. Sometimes the feelings of guilt and remorse are unbearable. But you must learn to handle these emotions. You need to find a way to calm yourself down and trudge through the storm. If you are a caregiver, you may need to help a patient with distress tolerance. This can be done by listening to her feelings, keeping them occupied with something, or giving them a massage. If you are a patient, you can learn to ride these rough waves by keeping yourself busy so that the ED thoughts are not playing loudly in your head.

Here are some things to say or do to deal with distress before, after, and during eating:

- ❁ Distractions! How many times has this come up? It's because they are so useful! Play a game, read a book, watch a movie, or have a conversation. Just keep yourself occupied so that ED cannot fill your head with negative thoughts and comments.

- Play music and let it silence your thoughts. Sing a song or read aloud.

- During a meal, you may suddenly feel very uncomfortable and squirm. You look down and see how much you ate, and you feel like a pig. You don't want to eat any more, even though you should. What do you do? In this case, use a distraction right away. Take a deep breath and remind yourself that this is for your own good. No one but you will suffer if ED kills you. No one but you will benefit if you restore your health by eating. This is all for you. You deserve to live a good life, even if that means being in pain and distress now. The discomfort will die down. Take another long, deep breath. You have come this far. You can do this. Just one bite at a time; it will soon be over.

- If you are a caregiver, you may hear the patient complaining that she is fat, ugly, and a failure for eating. Sometimes, you might find it easier to ignore her. At other times, the patient will get angry if you are not saying anything. This is tough because, again, it is basically a lose-lose situation. If you feel the need to say something, try something like, "I know ED is giving you a hard time for eating. But that means that you have done something he doesn't like. I am so proud of you. I know how hard that must have been for you, and I appreciate how brave you were. You are my hero. Now, let's go do XXX."

Remember that for patients, feeling "fat" is a very real feeling. I literally felt as though my body was expanding with every bite of food that I swallowed. But it was more than a feeling—it was like torture. I felt ashamed and sad that I was defying ED. I felt weak because I was giving in to the pressure of eating, and I knew that this would result in weight gain. ED made me feel horrible. He always called me fat. This is common for patients, who will say that they feel huge, fat, or "like a pig."

But wait . . . is "fat" really a feeling? Is it an emotion like happiness or sadness? The truth is that when a patient says that she feels fat, she is actually using this phrase to express other emotions. In my case, "feeling fat" meant that I was physically very full. Mentally, it meant that I was struggling because I knew that I was gaining weight. Emotionally, it meant that I was scared because I did not want to be made fun of for my weight and shape. It meant feeling regret and guilt that I ate all that food; that I would be overweight once again. This is why I was frustrated when others would tell me that I was not fat: when I looked into the mirror, I did not see a fat girl. But I did see a girl who was once overweight and had to work extremely hard to lose weight. I saw a girl who never wanted to gain weight because she was previously made fun of for her body. I saw a soul who struggled every day with these thoughts, fears, and miseries. I saw a small body that had taken years to get to where it is was now. I saw the days where I forbade myself to eat, out of a desire to look thinner and to stop all the teasing that I so often heard. I heard the rumbles of my stomach as I denied it food, hoping to achieve the "thin look." I saw the sufferings of a girl who had a constant voice in her head, telling her that she is going to get fat.

This is what patients often feel as well. Again, we are left with a lose-lose situation. Can you say anything to help the patient feel better? Sometimes, sadly, there is nothing you can do or say to help her. ED will make her feel fat regardless of what you say or do. It may be helpful for you to acknowledge that she feels fat, but to let her know that this is ED talking. Over time, these feelings will dwindle and become insignificant.

If you are a patient and are trying to take control over your recovery, you may begin to notice that you are gaining weight. If you are a caregiver, you will have to deal with the distress of a patient's gaining weight. This is extremely difficult for patients because it is a signal to ED that his power is weakening, and the patient is recovering. ED hates eating and weight gain. He despises it, and he will take any opportunity to make the patient feel remorse over this. Some parents feel that not telling patients their weight will help with this, whereas others believe that patients must learn that the number on the scale should not elicit such strong feelings and anxiety. What you do depends on your treatment team's and your own views.

As I mentioned before, my family and I decided that I would need to know my weight so that I could learn to live with it. I needed to realize that although I hated seeing the number go up, this was necessary for my recovery. I also had to learn that this number could not dictate my mood, self-worth, or value. My weight did not dictate how beautiful or intelligent I was. In this way, I was "exposed" to my weight, almost like the systemic desensitization I talked about before. Something to note about weight gain is that it is not always linear. In fact, the first week or so may show a very large gain, and this often causes a lot of anxiety and distress for patients. I gained seven pounds in my first week and I went crazy. I vowed to never eat again and I blamed myself and my family for making me fat. I said that I would never be able to eat normally again because my body would keep gaining weight and getting bigger.

My parents were a bit confused as well. How could I gain seven pounds in one week? Don't get me wrong—they were happy with the gain. But they were curious how this had happened. *Note that a quick weight gain can be a sign of water-loading or attempts to "fake" the gain. Always make sure that this is not occurring.*

Assuming the weight gain is "real," why did this happen? Will the patient always gain this much weight each week? And does this mean you need to give her less food so that she gains a more "reasonable" amount?

Think about the body: it has been starved for a long time. It had little or no fuel to perform all its functions. Now, you have given it some fuel. It is excited to finally have energy. The body is dehydrated, so it needs to replenish its store of fluids. Some pounds from the first weigh-ins can be attributed to water. The body has been deprived of fats, glucose, and proteins for a long time. Now that it's receiving food, it wants to fill up the stores in case it has to deal with starvation again. This is why the first few weigh-ins may show large gains. If the body receives enough nutrition consistently, the weight gain will slow down because the body will eventually realize that another famine isn't going to happen.

A normal weight gain is one to two pounds per week. Anything more may or may not be a sign of complications, and any less may be an indication that more food is needed. Caloric intakes vary from patient to patient, but it is commonly agreed that 3,500 calories per day is necessary to achieve this gain. This is because it takes around 3,500 extra calories to gain one pound. Again, this depends on the individual's metabolism, genes, how long she has been restricting, her age, medical history, etc. A medical team can give you a more accurate assessment.

To a certain extent, recovery really IS about the food. Sure, there are a lot of other things. But at the top of ED's "avoid list" is food. In recovery, it helps for the patient to realize that she has spent so much time and effort avoiding food, and that this made her ill. If a patient tells you "it's not always about the food," she is telling the truth: It is also about feelings, confidence, body image, and more. But for now, some focus has to be on the food. Be mindful that for someone with ED, eating is a huge fear. It will not be easy for her to sit down and eat meal after meal. This was hard for me at first, too. But over time, it got easier.

I'm sitting down at my kitchen table, facing my biggest fear. My worst nightmare. The enemy. My chest tightens; it is becoming hard to breathe. My heart is racing—I can almost hear it beating against my chest. My head is pounding. I cannot do this. I cannot face this horrible, wretched thing. Someone, make it stop! Take it away! Free me from this misery!

No, I'm not talking about a spider. Or some deadly bacteria. I'm talking about (can you guess?) . . . food. That's right. F-O-O-D. Yup. That's my fear. The only thing that makes me shiver, makes me want to run away and hide. And for so long, that is exactly what I did.

Having anorexia is not "all about the food"—there are lots of other issues, depending on the victim. But, to a great extent, it IS about the food and the weight gain. I spent countless days desperately trying to run away from any chance to eat. Of course, this sounds strange to many people. I mean, what happens when you get together with your friends? You eat. Or what does Grandma do as soon as you walk into her house? She feeds you (despite your reassuring her that you are full!). What happens on Easter and Christmas after church? We eat. Make no mistake—it is very difficult to run away from food.

But for people with AN, the ultimate goal is to avoid food because for them, it translates into immediate weight gain. I am guilty of this. Before every morsel that enters my mouth, I think about the weight gain behind it. I'm terrified that I will gain too much weight too quickly, that I will look "fat," that people will notice and make fun of me, that my clothes won't fit, that I'll have to diet all over again . . . AHH! The list never ends.

Please keep in mind that these feelings and thoughts are REAL. I do not make them up to seek attention or to be annoying. I really truly am afraid to eat. That is the essence of the illness. It lurks, just waiting for the time to eat. Then, it pounces on the victim, literally taking her life with it. ED does not want you to live; he wants you to die. To cease existing. It is ruthless; it will not stop until it gets what it wants—your life.

In my illness, I have told myself that I will stop "after I lose just these five pounds." But then I'd lose those, and want to lose more. Why? Because if five pounds could be lost, why couldn't ten? fifteen? thirty? But here's the paradox: The very thing that is avoided in AN is the same thing that must be consumed in order to recover—food.

When faced with a meal, I immediately want to RUN. To escape the pain that comes with eating. My body and my organs are screaming "Feed us!" but that nasty little fool in my head is saying, *"NO! No food. Do not eat. Stay strong. You do not need to eat. You will get fat."*

So, what to do? Do I eat and face the perils and sufferings of ED? Or do I listen to ED, not feel bad for eating, but then end up being sicker than before? Ah, here lies the hard decision: to eat or not to eat? Deep down, I know that I have to stay strong. Even if all my thoughts and feelings are arguing against me. Even if ED insists that I will gain weight. Even if ED makes me feel like a "fat pig." I have to eat. Because, as is often said, food is medicine. But HOW do I just ignore these things? It is not easy. It takes a lot of work. Keep up hope that one day, things will get better. It sounds easy; it is not. It is very difficult. It is a long road. But, "I can do all things through Christ who strengthens me" (Philippians 4:13). And that's enough to keep me going.

With consistent weight gain, the body's metabolism starts to fire up. Think about the metabolism as though it were a burning fire: If there is no wood, it cannot heat up. However, once you start giving it wood, the fire heats up. This is what happens in patients recovering from ED. At first, their basal metabolic rate will be slow because the body does this to adapt to low food amounts. When in restriction mode, the body slows down its functions in order to conserve energy. Once it starts getting food, it fires up and starts working overtime. This is often called "hyper-metabolism." When this occurs in a patient with ED, she may need even more food to gain weight. It is not uncommon for patients to need to consume 4,000-plus calories to achieve a one- or two-pound gain.

Bear in mind that not all patients experience this. It is somewhat easy to know when this is occurring because the patient will have eaten and retained all her food, yet her weight will not increase. This may be an indication that the body is in the hypermetabolic mode and needs more food. Remember that the food that you (or the patient) are eating is going toward many different processes. The body needs food to store fat and glycogen. Muscles need to be built. Energy must be supplied. Hair, nails, and skin need to grow. Now think about the inside: cell membranes must be built, hormones need to function, and neurotransmitters must be synthesized. Simply contracting your muscles and breathing requires energy! Your brain relies completely on glucose for energy, so it needs all the food it can get.

For growing bodies, nutrition is needed for puberty and growth, including sexual characteristics. For females who have not yet started menarche, fuel is needed for this process. In fact, a certain level of fat is needed in the diet for menstruation to start; in females with amenorrhea, enough fat is needed for menstruation to resume.

It is truly amazing to think of how much food recovering patients need. When I was eating to gain weight, I doubted that my body needed all of that food but when I thought about how much was going on inside of my body, it made sense! It was as though my bodily functions and organs were fighting for any piece of food and energy that they could get. It was only fair that I eat enough for all of them!

One more thing to keep in mind is that the body has a tendency to lay down fat before muscle. It commonly does this in the stomach or abdominal area, which is why the patient might complain that her stomach has gotten larger, which can actually be very distressing for her to see. The patient often sees this, along with the quick weight gain, and begins to give up. She may stop eating because she is too distressed. BUT THIS IS WRONG! Do not let her do this, and do not be discouraged! These are normal signs along the path to recovery: the weight gain will slow down, and the weight will redistribute! The body will begin shifting the weight, water, fat, and muscle to other parts like the arms, legs, and thighs. As time goes by, the weight will even out.

As the body's metabolism starts to work again, some changes may occur in the patient. First, she will likely have a lot more energy. This is a good thing, but remember that she needs to conserve as much energy as she can in order for her body to heal. The issue of when to allow patients to exercise is a common question among caregivers and patients alike. A treatment team can best determine when, and how much, physical activity can be included. Too much exercising can become addictive for patients, and it also burns calories. More calories burned means that the body doesn't have enough fuel to use for its processes, so the patient needs to eat even more. To an extent, some physical activity may be safe—ask your team.

When I had about five pounds left to gain, I was given permission to include light exercise. However, this had to be limited so that my body would not burn too many calories—after all, I was already eating a lot and could not stand the thought of having to eat more. I started off by including light leisure activities such as walking or playing badminton. However, if a patient had previously felt compelled to exercise, this might make it unsafe for her to begin activity again. Always check with your team and remember to set reasonable limits.

A common complaint among patients during re-feeding is night sweats. This happens because the body is now working overtime and generates more heat. This can even happen during the day, and patients may complain of feeling warm or hot. I definitely had night sweats during re-feeding—and this was something that many other patients could relate to. Why do patients sweat so much at night? A starved anorexic is . . . well, a starved person. The body has the ability to compensate for this lack of food by lowering the metabolism. This is one reason why a patient, when ill, is cold all the time: Instead of wasting energy on keeping her warm, her body decides to use that valuable energy to keep her brain, heart, and organs alive. Hence, her metabolism slows down. This is why she could gain a lot of weight even after eating a little bit of food in early recovery: her body is scared that a period of famine will come again, so it wants to store all it can just in case this happens. However, after some time of re-feeding, her body will "wake up." The body will realize that food is consistently coming, so it can afford to keep her warm. The annoying and uncomfortable part of this is that she may get sweaty at night. This can be very uncomfortable for her, especially if she needs to get up at night to change her clothes or bedsheets. As terrible as this sounds, it is a good sign that her body is getting back to normal functioning and it recognizes that it can now keep her warm. Like many other things in recovery (and I'll say this A LOT!), night sweats stink (pun intended!). They are such a nuisance, but they are a good sign that health is on its way.

Remember that recovery is not a straight and simple road. There will be some days when you will not mind eating and will feel fine. Then there will be days when you feel tired, angry, and fat. These days are hard to deal with because you don't want them to interfere with your recovery and progress. At the same time, you feel terrible and simply don't want to eat more. ED may be trying to sneak back into your life and take over your thoughts. He is angry that you are recovering and getting better. His power is weakening, and he feels it. He is doing all he can to hold onto you and pull you back under his wing. But during these times, you must not give in. You must remember how far you have come and how much you have achieved. When you don't feel like eating, remember what starvation did to your health. When you don't want to keep the food down, remember how weak you were when you didn't have enough food for your body.

Something that I found helpful during recovery was to keep a "feeling-food log." What I did was write in my feelings after I ate—how I felt fat and like a failure. Then I wrote down a response to my own feelings, and I thought of what I could do to make myself feel better. Here is an example of two days about a year apart. Notice how one year later, I am able to identify the discomfort associated with eating, but I don't let it bother me. I realize that ED is trying to sabotage my recovery, and writing this helps me reflect on its truth.

Date, time	Feeling	Reflection: What I can do to/think feel better
July 24, 2012 2:00 p.m. (after lunch)	I feel fat for eating my entire lunch, even though no one was there to make me eat it.	I know I did the right thing by eating even though I was alone. I feel lousy now, but that's ED trying to make me regret being healthy. As a distraction, I'm going to play a game with my dad.

Date, time	Feeling	Reflection: What I can do to/think feel better
March 16, 2013 10:30 a.m. (after breakfast)	I'm really full after eating my breakfast. Yesterday I was weighed, and my weight is up again. I feel awful and want to cry and be alone.	I know that I probably feel so sad and angry now because ED is mad that my weight is up. He is calling me fat. But I know that I'm not fat—I am gaining the weight that I need to be healthy. I am full, but that is a normal feeling. It will pass by. Instead of focusing on how full I feel, I am going to read a book.

As the weight comes on, the patient may start to feel nervous that people will notice the change in her body shape. How will she face people? What if others comment on how much weight she has gained, or how much "better" she looks now? Better means bigger, doesn't it? What happens when everyone starts to stare at her because she is eating? Remember that people don't usually comment on weight—and if they do, instruct the patient to ignore them. It is easy to say this but difficult to practise. But she must remember that her weight is her own business, and gaining weight means that she is healthy. HEALTHY, NOT FAT. If people do comment and tell her how nice she looks now, she need not be offended. People do not mean to harm her—they truly believe that she looks healthier now. Of course, ED will interpret this as meaning that she looks fat now. It is your job to help silence ED and to help the patient to understand that when she was sick, she looked fragile and skeletal. Now, she looks healthy, strong, and beautiful.

One difficult part about recovery is saying goodbye to the old, small clothes and buying new, bigger clothes. Almost all patients with ED go through this, and it is a challenge. Letting go of your smaller clothes means that you have gained enough weight and they no longer fit. This means that you are not "thin" anymore. This means that others will notice how large you have become. Now, when you buy clothes, you will no longer fit into the smallest size. You will actually be too BIG for some sizes. And that thought scares you. Everyone promised that they wouldn't make you fat, but you feel fat now. It is not fair—why couldn't you have stayed thin enough to wear these clothes again? And what if you gain more weight? Will you have to buy more clothes, this time in an even bigger size? It is hard. I struggled with this a lot.

Sometimes, however, it is neither feasible nor economical to keep purchasing new clothes. In these cases, you may find it helpful to purchase recycled clothes at a lower cost (for example, from Value Village) or to ask family and friends for clothes that they are not using. Whatever you do, remember that getting rid of your small clothes is a good thing because it signifies how much healthier you are now. And you will not be tempted to try to fit in them again.

When I gained weight and tried to put on my old dresses, I couldn't bring them up past my knees. I was horrified. I screamed and cried, and refused to leave the house. I sat in my closet with my old clothes around me, terrified at the huge person I had become. My sister came in and noticed how distressed I was. She offered to take me shopping to buy new clothes, but I said that I didn't want anything new. I wanted *these* clothes in *these* small sizes. Then, my sister told me something that struck a chord with me: These clothes, she said, were not normal clothes. They were very small, and the only reason we bought them was because my normal-sized clothes were too big and falling off of my body. My family was not happy to have purchased these small sizes, but they had to because everything else was too big for me. Essentially, these small clothes were my "sick and unhealthy" clothes. My sister told me that my healthier body was beautiful, and that I would find many clothes to wear in stores.

But I still complained, saying that now I had lost many beautiful clothes and that I did not even have the courage to try things on. My sister comforted me by acknowledging my distress and she offered to buy me clothes when she went to the mall and bring them home so that I wouldn't have to try them on in the store. (This is, in fact, what many parents do. Another tip is to buy clothes and remove the size tag if the patient is anxious about sizes.) When I really thought it over, I decided that she was right. Part of me was still angry and frustrated that I couldn't wear these clothes anymore, but the other part of me felt that buying new clothes would help me accept my new, heavier—no, healthier—body. We gave away my old clothes to charity, and this also helped me feel better about the process. Going on a shopping spree to buy new clothes was exciting, even if at first choosing bigger sizes was harder. Eventually,

I learned that clothes sizes are not important. Some of my pants are size 8 in one company, and at another store, I wear size 30 pants. At one store, I am a medium for tops, but at another, I am an extra-large. I learned to treat my clothes sizes like I do my shoe sizes—I don't really care what size I am, as long as the clothes (or shoes) fit comfortably, look nice, and make me feel good.

Let's wrap this chapter up with a note about accepting your new body. In recovery, it is unlikely that you will be thrilled with your new body. Yes, it will be healthier. But it will also be heavier, and ED hates that. It is different for you to be heavier, since you have been so deadly thin for a while. Part of recovery means that you have to learn to accept and appreciate your body. You need not consider yourself a sexy beast (although you can, if that works for you . . .), but you should realize that when you made the decision to recover from ED, it was the right choice. Your body is now stronger, healthier, and beautiful.

As I recovered, buying clothes was one challenge. Another challenge was looking at myself in the mirror and actually liking what I saw. I was so disgusted with my weight gain that I failed to see how much my healthy body allowed me to do. That is when I decided that it was time to expose myself to my body. To think about it and how amazingly strong it now was. To appreciate how it got me to places, helped me play sports, and allowed me to complete daily tasks. It wasn't easy, but I found ways to help me do so.

"Body exposure" is a term used to describe the process whereby patients with ED learn to accept their bodies. It is made worse when the patient tries to avoid her body. For example, she might not wear a swimsuit so that she will not need to see her body or skin. She may avoid mirrors; or dress in the dark. It sounds drastic, but this goes to show how extreme this hatred or fear of the body can be. Body exposure can be done in many ways. Some suggest staying in front of a mirror and staring, while avoiding making negative comments. To be honest, this does not work for me. A mirror should ONLy be for looking to check how you look before going out—nothing more. So, staring in front of a mirror actually makes me a lot more uncomfortable. However, this leaves me stuck without a solution to my body image issues.

One way that has helped me tremendously is massage therapy. I absolutely LOVE getting massages, as they really make me relax. My muscles feel calm, and I can forget about all the troubles in this world. Interestingly, research actually shows that massages are helpful in the treatment of EDs. The reasons for this may vary, but generally, massages help a person relax. For me, this makes me appreciate how tired my body is and it helps me understand just how much my body has done for me throughout the day. It also helps to take my mind off the day and it puts me in a calm mood.

Patients with ED might enjoy getting therapeutic massages, or even participating in other pampering activities such as pedicures. Or, save money and have a partner, friend, or family member give the patient a relaxing back rub! What about getting together with a few friends and practising mindfulness or yoga together! Whatever is done, the focus should be for the patient to learn to see her body in a new light, to accept and appreciate her stronger body, and to learn to cope with her new size. This will take time, and it may not be enjoyable at first. As time goes on, she will begin to understand that her new body, although heavier, is also stronger and healthier.

Chapter Eight

Pour some cheer-up
on those recovery pancakes

Sometimes it seems that the work in recovery never ends. You've come so far: You have eaten, gained weight, and can eat on your own. You don't particularly love your new body, but you have learned to accept it the way it is. You are pursuing your dreams and you feel stronger, healthier, and happier. But deep down, you know that you can never forget what you have been through because of ED. You know that at any time, ED can sneak back up on you. That is why you need to make sure you are armed whenever he decides to annoy you.

Do you consider yourself (or the patient) recovered now? Is there such a thing as recovery? What does it look/feel like? Recovery means different things to different people. To me, it means that I am at a healthy weight, am eating normally and enough, and can move on with my life. I don't have to pretend that ED never happened, but I am stronger now. I might still get ED thoughts, but I never act on them. I can identify these thoughts and stop them before they spiral out of control.

But is recovery a destination—something that you reach, and then it's over? Or does it continue for the rest of your life? To me, recovery is not a destination. It is more of a lifelong adventure. It is not some point that I will arrive at and then "be done with it." It is something that I need to work on for the rest of my life. I do not starve myself or restrict food, but I still do not feel hungry. I still do not really enjoy eating like others do. I need to keep working on recovery, each day getting stronger and stronger.

I'm learning new things about recovery each day. For example, the other day, someone made a rude comment to me regarding my body size. In the older days, this would have caused me to restrict and not eat. As angry and sad as I was, I did not do this. I still ate. I was angry, but I ate. I did not give in to ED. There are still things I am uncomfortable with. I hate it when my clothes feel tighter. I hate looking in the mirror and seeing myself bigger than I used to be. I get uncomfortable when people remind me that I am eating a lot. This is why recovery is a lifelong adventure. There are ups and downs. There are times when I am strong, and times when I feel weak. There are moments when ED is not there, and there are others when his voice creeps back in.

Recovery is better seen as a job—I know this sounds tiresome, but it is true. It is what I do. My wages for recovery are the improvements in my health and life. The hard work I do in recovery is part of my job. But the rewards are worth every struggle, every tear, and every fight. Each day in recovery makes me aware of how much work it is. It takes a lot out of a person to recover from ED. It is truly a full-time job. But it helps when you have a family that is willing to be there for you 24/7. It is humbling to know that you have a God who watches over you every second. It is empowering to see yourself transforming into a stronger and more knowledgeable person.

Recovery is definitely not a destination. It is an adventure. But it is an adventure that I would never give up on. Because each day in recovery helps me realize how much of my life I deserve to get back. A helpful exercise for the patient to complete is to think of all the things she has gained (no pun intended!) from recovery. This will assist caregivers, as well as the patient, to reflect on how much recovery was worth the fight.

At times, you (or the caregiver) might feel frustrated that you still have to deal with ED. You may still feel angry that you have gained all that weight. Sometimes, you might wonder why life isn't suddenly easier. Wasn't recovery supposed to do wonders for you and for your family? Didn't everyone say that you would be happier when you ate and gained weight? Then why do you feel so lousy and stressed now? Remember that recovery is something you always need to be working on, and that this is one part of your life—and that of your caregivers. There will always be challenges along the way, whether related to ED or to other things such as school, work, relationships, obligations, and more. Recovering from ED does not mean that you are invincible to pain or challenges. But it

DOES mean that you are stronger and healthier, so you will be better able to face those obstacles and tackle them. Don't expect for all of life to be simple once you have gotten better—instead, expect that you will be able to meet life's difficult demands now that you are well.

One of these days in recovery, you are bound to reflect on how far you have come. You may think back to when you were sick and how your life has changed since then. I recently did this, and I was shocked at the way I felt. Part of me felt proud of what I had accomplished in my life since I decided to recover. I felt pleased with how much stronger and healthier I was now. But a part of me ached at what I had been through. I looked at my experiences with getting sick with ED and how much I suffered. It hurt a lot. I pictured myself as a young girl, and my mind raced through all my experiences with bullying, starvation, teasing, and self-hatred. I began to feel sorry for that little Marina, the little girl who had to endure so much teasing because of her weight. I felt miserable that a young girl like me felt the need to starve herself just so that she could be thin and put an end to people's taunting.

At this point, I was crying. Why did I have to go through this? Everyone has problems, but why did I have to get the eating disorder? What had I ever done to deserve this? I expressed my feelings to my father, who was able to remind me of something that I had forgotten: Yes, maybe I was the one who had to deal with ED. Yes, I was the victim of a terrible illness that robbed me of my body, health, and happiness. It had been very difficult, and it was painful for me to endure. But on the brighter side, it made me stronger. It made me realize that my body deserves care and has dignity. It opened my eyes to the unrealistic expectations that others and I have had for myself. It helped me appreciate my body and health. All in all, though ED was tough, my experiences turned me into the strong, intelligent, informed, healthy, and motivated young woman I am today. Instead of feeling sorry for myself, I learned to view my experiences in a positive light.

A vital part of recovering from ED is learning to express emotions. Many people with eating disorders struggle with letting their feelings out. In fact, sometimes it is even hard for me to admit that I am "feeling" something. As I mentioned before, ED makes the patient numb: She doesn't feel pain, happiness, or excitement. ED makes her entirely focused on restricting and losing weight, so that nothing else is important. During recovery, this begins to change. As I got better, I felt a flood of feelings overwhelm me—and I didn't know how to react to them. When I felt down, was I sad or angry? Was I frustrated or just tired, and what caused this? I could not say. A patient with ED will tell you the same thing—she doesn't know HOW she feels! Having a list of feelings can be useful here because it aids the patient in pinpointing exactly what she is feeling. I made a chart for myself, listing what happened and how it affected my mood. This was very eye-opening because it helped me see the connections between events in my life and my emotions.

There are a lot of "feeling" words out there, so learning to identify what exactly you are feeling is useful. Equally important is expressing these feelings. When I was ill, I never talked about what bothered me because I wanted to be alone. ED isolated me and made me shut everyone out, including my family. As I got better, I felt so many different emotions and I could not stand to be alone. I wanted to share this with someone, to talk about my feelings and have someone listen to me. If you feel that a therapist is necessary, maybe you should go to one and try it out. I did this for a while, until I learned to master expressing my emotions. My family also took the time to educate themselves, and they became very supportive.

When I was little, we never expressed emotions at home. If someone felt sad, we did not talk about it for fear of ruining everyone else's mood. If I was angry, I was not free to openly express it. After ED, things changed. My family learned the importance of letting your feelings out in a safe environment. This is critical! If you feel angry, let it out! You will feel a lot better, and this way, one bad feeling will not build on another. Sharing your feelings with someone supportive is freeing because you no longer feel alone. Sometimes, we don't want advice or a practical voice of reason or knowledge—all we need is someone to listen and to understand. Throughout your recovery, make sure that you have at least one person who is available and willing to listen to how you feel. When I was ill, I did not think that I was "good enough" or deserved to feel certain emotions. I felt as though sharing my emotions was a waste of time and something that I was not worthy of. Again, this is because of ED. As I recovered, I realized that the more I talked about my emotions, the less they haunted me, and the better I felt.

Recovering from an eating disorder is a big deal. I mean, it's a really BIG deal. I have always been an independent person, and recovery was no different. I wanted to do it alone, to show everyone that I could recover without anyone's help. But it simply did not work that way. Yes, I was the only one who could eat and do the weight gaining. Yes, I was the only one who had to ignore ED's taunts. But I needed the support of those around me, and the care and love others could provide. Even after I recovered, part of me still wanted to be independent. I did not want others to see me as the girl who had to get help for an eating disorder. I was worried that my family and friends would look upon me as being weak and not having the ability to do things on my own. This made me determined to do everything else on my own.

I would cook, clean, and study on my own. I never asked anyone for help for anything because I wanted to prove that I was not a baby who needed people to do things for me. I wanted others to see that I, Marina, did not need others for support or help. I was a big girl and I did not need any help. You can imagine how much damage this did in my life. It put a lot of pressure on me because I refused to get any assistance with anything. It meant that things took twice the amount of time to complete because no one was doing it with me. I wanted to prove my independence, but it was taking a toll on my life.

One day, I cracked. I could not stand doing anything without any help. I told my mom that I was frustrated and felt trapped. One part of me wanted to assert my independence, but the other part of me was tired of doing everything on my own and not being able to ask for help. My mom was very understanding. She explained to me that everyone in the world needs help eventually—whether it is assistance with lifting something, asking for a favour, or even getting advice. She used an expression that I will never forget: *A bag has two handles for a reason—so that two people can lift it together.* This struck a chord with me. I realized that asking for help was not a sign of weakness, but of strength. I am not saying that I am not strong enough to do this on my own, but that the workload is too much and that extra help would save me a lot of effort and time.

A personality trait that seems to be common in patients with ED is perfectionism. You know, the feeling that everything needs to be just exactly right; that there is no room for failure or mistakes. I struggled with this a lot, before, during, and even after ED. As a child, I kept my room very organized. My toys were always put away, and my closet was divided into sections by colours. As a teen, I always meticulously finished my homework and made sure my books were crisp and clean.

Even now, I still have the urge to fix that crooked picture frame or straighten up the messy table. At times, this can be a good thing because it ensures that you put forth your best effort. But at other times, it gets tedious and annoying. It also puts a lot of pressure on me to always be a high achiever. I always feel the need to get very high marks — a B+ simply isn't good enough for me. I must make the honour roll. I need to be the perfect daughter, student, nurse, sister, and friend. Clearly, these are unrealistic expectations.

At other times, perfectionism manifests in not knowing how to take breaks. I study all day and night because I feel like a failure and a lazy individual if I don't. I practise my clinical skills until I am exhausted because I feel guilty if I take a break. It is not uncommon for me to go through an entire day without having any fun or relaxing moments. Over time, this builds up. Day after day of working and not taking breaks starts to stress me out.

A patient with ED usually feels this way. She may feel as though she needs to study or work really hard, and she feels that taking breaks means she is lazy and is worried that relaxing for a while means that she is not fulfilling her duties as an employee or student. When I was ill, this was an issue. I tried to ignore my hunger pains by focusing on school and work. Nothing else mattered as long as I could get high marks. But to do so meant that I had to study for twenty-four hours a day. I did not want to take any breaks because I feared that doing so would make me get a lower mark. Even in recovery, I felt that there was no room for breaks. I had to do all my work, finish my CBT homework, and then sleep. There was no time to be wasted on having fun or taking breaks.

Finally, I realized how unrealistic this was. Everyone needs a break once in a while! Taking time away from my work doesn't make me a lazy student or worker — it means that I am human! You can be surprised at what a good break does. It can make you feel refreshed and prepared to tackle the next assignment or task.

Remember back when I mentioned distress tolerance? You may be wondering why it is appearing in this part of the book, assuming that you have now mastered the ability to handle negative feelings around food. Well, part of distress tolerance is learning how to handle tough situations without reverting back to restriction. Many patients with ED will say that when they feel stressed or panicked, the ED thoughts become loud again. It is as though a difficult or stressful situation is a trigger for the eating disorder to take control again.

Do not downplay this, because this is often the cause of many relapses. When I was recovering, something that nearly caused me a relapse was when I had to study for a major exam. It was too stressful for me, and I felt ED getting loud again. My first thought was to restrict my food, as though this would take away my anxiety about the test.

In fact, sometimes patients can be doing really well in recovery, but all it takes is something stressful or difficult to trigger a relapse. Now that you know this, become aware. Realize and anticipate that tough times are inevitable in life. Restricting and listening to ED will not make these obstacles disappear. ED might, in fact, try to convince you that he can take your anxiety away if you just skip that one snack. DO NOT LISTEN. Understand that these challenges are common, but the way to handle them is not by falling back into ED's traps. Instead, make a plan on how you can deal with the situation. Ask others for help. Make sure you let ED know that when tough times strike, meals are still eaten. When faced with a challenge, restricting is not an option.

Now that you are moving on with your life and progressing through recovery, there might be times when you want to talk about your eating disorder to others. You might want to advocate or share your story to inspire others. But on the other hand, you are worried that this will make you look weak. You don't want people to think less of you because you have struggled with an eating disorder. There are different ways of approaching this. Some families and patients don't tell anyone what they have struggled with, while others decide that it is best for people to understand their circumstances.

In my case, telling people about ED was part of my goal as I recovered. I wanted to use my experiences to help others. But I was only able to do this once I had recovered for a solid period of time without any symptoms. You decide what is best for you. But always remember that no matter what, your experiences with ED do not make you weak or inferior to others. Your fight with this monster has made you a stronger and more aware person. You don't have to tell anyone about it if you do not want to. However, never feel ashamed of what you have experienced in terms of the eating disorder. No one has the right to judge you or think less of you because of this mental illness. No one has the right to tell you that you aren't good enough because you struggled with ED. Don't let anyone make you feel weak or inferior because you have dealt with a mental illness.

Many people have asked me similar questions: "How can you openly speak about your ED?" or, "Aren't you scared that people will know about you having ED and judge you?" Others ask, "What if people will not give you a job because of your history with ED?" So, I will start answering them!

1. I can speak openly about ED because I am not ashamed of it. I no longer am sick and am working my way through a solid recovery. I speak about it because so many others are scared to do so. EDs, like other mental illnesses, have so much stigma attached to them. And this should not be the case. An illness is not a person's fault. It bothers me when people are scared to speak about mental illnesses because this reflects the stereotypical stigma associated with them. I am frustrated with the lack of understanding and empathy that people have toward illnesses. Moreover, many people do not know about ED. They know what anorexia is, for example, but they do not know how serious/harmful/painful it is. I want to help raise awareness. I want the world to know that ED is a genuine, serious illness. Along with this, I want to give people hope that recovery is possible. That ED is not the end of life. By speaking about it openly, I hope to give people strength and courage to continue their fight, or to help others fight.

2. If people judge me because of my history with ED, then the problem is theirs, not mine. Like I said, ED is a mental illness. I am recovering, and that is all that counts. My history with ED does not make me weak; it makes me stronger. It shows the world that I have endured my battles and have come out as a winner. People who judge me because of my history with ED do not understand that my journey has made me a stronger and wiser person. Moreover, some people will ALWAYS find something wrong with you, regardless of how "perfect" you are. My place on earth is not to please others, but to glorify God in what I do. I believe that my journey with ED has helped me

help others and to raise awareness; and I thank God for His mercy with me.

3. This relates to the first two, but I will elaborate. Yes, I am a nursing student, soon to be a nurse. And YES, I had an eating disorder. So what? I became sick, just like anyone else could have. I am no longer symptomatic, and I am healthy. I am also a stronger person. My experiences with ED made me realize how much help people need, especially patients who are ill. This has taught me that patients need empathy, good care, and hope. That is what a good nurse does. I can now empathize with patients more and I understand the value of good, compassionate nursing care. I am a better nurse, person, and student because of my experiences with ED.

    So, while people might look at my history with ED as a weakness, I view it as a strength. People who judge others because of their history, illnesses, or weaknesses do this wrongly and unjustly. It is time we look past these superficial things and real- ize that we are stronger because of our experiences and illnesses. God says, "My grace is sufficient for you: for My strength is made perfect in weakness" (2 Corinthians 12:9).

So, recovery seems to be going well for you. Great news! Then, you real- ize that Christmas is coming soon. Or Ramadan. Or Passover. Basically, it is the time of year when your faith community fasts. What do you do? You have recovered (or are recovering) from ED, which means that you need to eat sufficient food with a great deal of variety. How on earth are you supposed to eliminate meats, cheeses, chocolate, and eggs? Or fast all day, not eating anything from morning until night? This issue is a common problem that a patient struggles with because she feels stuck. On one hand, she wants to fast because everyone else is doing it, and she doesn't want to feel as though she is not doing her part for her faith. But, on the other hand, she knows that fasting is not a wise thing to do with ED, even if she is recovered or almost there.

This happened to me. I am Coptic Orthodox, and we fast on and off for most of the year. What was I supposed to do during these times? Could I not eat? What if that triggered ED again? But if I didn't fast, I would feel left out. I would also be ashamed if others knew. If you are a caregiver or patient who is contemplating the same issue, consider these points about fasting and feasting for religious purposes. Then you can make an informed decision.

Fasting

In my religion, we fast on many occasions: Christmas, Easter, etc. These fasts can be as short as three days to as long as three months! The absolute strictest observance is to go without any food from the morning until around six p.m., which is when the Liturgy is held and we can take communion. If one cannot go this long without any food, then milk, dairy products, and meat are withheld instead. In some cases, fish is allowed (depending on the fasting occasion).

I know what you are thinking: How does someone with ED do this? Well, it all comes down to the person. God does not desire for us to fast and hurt our bodies in the process; rather, fasting is seen as a way for humans to realize that they need to control their worldly desires. For example, the point of fasting is to realize that as humans, we need to control our habit of sinning. By not eating, we are showing ourselves that if we can go for a while not eating and feeling hungry, we can most definitely take the steps to stop committing wrong deeds.

However, I want to make a distinct and important point here: GOD LOOKS AT THE HEART. Thus, for someone like me who is recovering, I can make a plan with my Father of Confession (a priest at my church) and decide that instead of fasting, I will (for example) memorize a Psalm every week and take the steps necessary to stop being rude to others. But if I can fast without harming my body, I do.

But sometimes, fasting for an entire day might be hard for us, especially for someone who is recovering from ED. Keeping in mind that God looks at the heart, we realize that it does no good if someone is fasting all day, yet they are nevertheless lying, sinning, and being rude and mean. What is the point, then, in such a case, of fasting? None whatsoever.

Thus, to each her own. If you can fast, then go for it. If you cannot, do not fear that God will be harsh to you or that you have failed; rather, realize that it is your actions that are most important. "It is not what goes into a man's mouth that harms him, but rather, what comes out of it" (Matthew 15:11).

Feasting

So, the church has been fasting for a month now, and everyone is ready to eat some good chicken, cheese, milk, and chocolate. These feasts usually occur late in the day (around eleven p.m. or midnight) because that is when the Liturgy for that occasion ends. Typically, people have no problem eating this late because they just want to taste some of the good food that they have not eaten for a while. But what is someone with ED to do? Do I eat at this occasion and feel guilty, or not eat enough? Or can I not eat and hope that people will understand? The most important (and best) decision that I made about feasts was this: help people to understand what I am going through, what I will do, and how they can help.

For me, this means that I usually do not eat during feasts at around midnight. Why? This is very important: IT IS NOT THAT I AM RESTRICT-ING. Rather, since I do not feel hungry at the specified times when I need to eat, I will definitely not be hungry at midnight, since I will have eaten a meal a couple of hours ago (bedtime snack).

At first, I would be really worried about how I would handle these feasts. Then, after talking to my family (my biggest support system!), I realized that I do not need to worry about these events. Getting together with my family to celebrate Easter or Christmas is wonderful, but it is NOT ALL ABOUT THE FOOD. If we were getting together at around dinnertime (say, six p.m.), I would definitely eat because that is when I would normally have my next meal. But I could not skip my dinner at six p.m. just so that I could eat a bigger meal at midnight. In recovery, I need to keep my mealtimes consistent so that my body is assured that it is going to get what it needs.

From another perspective, knowing what is going to be served at these celebrations helps me to plan my meals. If we are going to have a meal that is consistent with my lifestyle, maybe I can try something there. If not, then I will bring my own food to ensure that I am eating what I need. Maybe this sounds weird, but to be honest, it does not matter to me. I am at the stage in my life when I really do not worry what others may think or say, because I know that my health and happiness depend on my recovery's being solid. I need to do what I need to do to keep myself healthy, strong, and happy. If that means bringing my own food to celebrations or eating at my own mealtimes to ensure I am getting enough, so be it.

Note: this is the way I handle things. If you have ED and have a team, maybe they will suggest something different to you. Do what works best for YOU, not what others say is best for them. Although recovery from ED is working toward similar goals (e.g., to eat well, to be healthy and happy, to have less ED thoughts), there is not just ONE WAY to do things. I learned what works best for me, and this is what I do. I let my loved ones know how I am handling situations so that they can support me and realize that I need to do what my health depends on. And to be honest, if you have people who love and care for you, they will not care about when you eat your meals and what you eat (as long as you are eating enough and what you need) — they will just be happy and thankful that you are present to celebrate an event with them. Always remember that in the Bible, God reminds us that, "the Lord doesn't see things the way [humans] see them. People judge by outward appearance, but the Lord looks at the HEART" (1 Samuel 16:7).

***

Somewhere along your journey to recovery, you may find it helpful to see a therapist if you haven't already. Therapists can help you deal with your thoughts, feelings, and behaviours. Before you see a therapist, however, remember that you need to know what and how they feel about eating disorders, as this will influence how they treat you. Many patients find that CBT — cognitive behaviour therapy — is especially useful because it helps them notice how their thoughts affect their feelings. As a nursing student, I had a strong background in psychology, so I already knew a lot about CBT. I decided to try following CBT at home. With the help of my parents and sister, we were able to use CBT principles to change the way we thought, felt, and behaved. If you can afford a therapist, this might be an easier option for you; others have insurance coverage. In my case, it wasn't that I couldn't afford one, but rather that I could not find a therapist who specialized in ED. All the therapists I saw had strange beliefs about eating disorders, such as theories that my mother caused it because she was overprotective, or that ED was a way for me to cope with life and rebel against my parents. If your therapist shares these views, it should be a red flag that he/she are not right for you. (Please see chapter thirteen for more information.)

One of the most helpful things my family and I learned was our ABCs. No, not the alphabet! Rather, ABC is a useful way of determining *what happened, why it happened*, and *why you acted in a certain way*. This was applicable to many parts of our lives, especially when we all felt stressed or angry. As a patient who suffered from ED, using the ABC model helped me pinpoint the reasons for my behaviour; in turn, this helped me to learn from my experiences and to anticipate future challenges. I learned to reflect on my actions and see what I might do better the next time.

What are the ABCs? Well . . .

A is for Antecedent

This is what has happened before, or the situation that you are in. This is important because it determines what is going on around you. It could be anything—good or bad. Maybe you have received a bad mark on a test, or perhaps you got into a fight with a friend or loved one. Or perhaps work is stressful, or you have too much to do. On the other hand, it could be something good, as is the case when you hear good news. Whatever happens, this determines your feelings or reactions. How do you feel about this situation? What is going through your head? What has happened that made you feel this way?

B is for Behaviour

This is actually what you do (or did), and it is guided by what occurs (the antecedent). What are you going to do about the situation? What actions will you take? Maybe you are so stressed about your job that you accidentally take it out on your spouse and kids. Or maybe you feel hopeless because of your marks so you give up studying for the next test. Or, perhaps you feel happy about your promotion and you celebrate with your family and friends, or you are thankful to God for being with you so you donate some money to the needy. Do you see how the behaviour is related to the situation? The behaviour, while it may seem easy, is difficult at times to control. We need to think about what we are going to do because it has implications for the future. Sometimes we make good choices, but at other times, we don't. We may be impulsive and do things that we regret. Our behaviours at times might surprise us because they are not what we are used to. At other times, we might make decisions that seem to be right, only to learn that they were not the best choices we could have made.

C is for Consequences

This is what happens when you actually do what you have decided to do. What happened after you acted? Was it what you expected—good or bad? Was anyone hurt or bothered by what you did? Are you pleased with how you handled the situation? This is important because reflection allows us to realize what we did wrong and what we did right. By weighing the pros and cons of what we did, we can begin to see what we would do the next time and how this will be different than how we acted before. We learn this way because we can analyze our actions and the consequences they have for our lives. What would you do differently the next time? What did you do that you would do again? How was it helpful, or not helpful? Reflecting like this also helps us make decisions for the future. It allows us to learn from our experiences so that next time, we can remember how our actions impacted us and decide if this is what we will do again.

Give this a try! You will be surprised by how much you learn about yourself, as well as from your experiences. You may begin to see a pattern in how you make decisions, and this can help you make wiser or better choices in the future. It can also help you recognize what you value, what you believe in, and what your priorities are.

Whether or not you are seeing a therapist, you may realize that there are some things that need to change at home or with your family. Therapists can be useful for this, too. In my family, we had difficulty (as I mentioned before) expressing emotions. After I recovered, we realized that we needed to find a healthy way to listen and to respond to one another's emotions. In particular, I needed others to be around to support me when I felt down. I needed my family to understand that I had moments when I felt fat, ugly, useless, and hopeless. So, I decided to tell my family about these feelings. I had to explain to them that sometimes I don't need advice from them. All I need is a listening ear. Here were some things that I mentioned to them; please note that this may not work for everyone. I have included this as an example of how you can communicate with your family to let them understand how to help you. As such, each person's feelings, thoughts, and ways of coping may be entirely unique. In any case, you will be surprised at how helpful it is when loved ones understand how to respond to your feelings or struggles. It also helps them cope with your distress and provide support.

When I feel "fat"

If someone I know tells me that I have not gained any weight, I'll stare at them because I know they are not telling the truth. I *have* gained weight (a lot) and I know it's obvious—so telling me that I don't look fat will only make things worse.

What *will* help is for the person to listen. I want him or her to know that this feeling is very real. I feel fat and big and ugly. That's part of my illness. It bothers me because it makes me feel like a failure. What would help is for the person to understand that feeling fat (to me) is distressing and angering. I need that person to know that even if I don't *look* fat, I *feel* fat. What is helpful is for the person to say, "Yes, you gained weight. But you are not fat or overweight. If you were, I would be honest and tell you because I care. I would not tell you that you weren't overweight if you really were. I would tell the truth."

When I feel sad

Sometimes I'm tired, sad, and frustrated. I get so busy with all my work and recovery that I'm irritable. At times like this, I want someone to understand how hard my life is. Yes, some people are in far worse situations, but I've been through quite a lot. I don't always want to hear, "It will get better." Sometimes I want to hear, "I know that you have so much on your mind right now. And I can't even imagine how tired and sad you must feel. If I can help with anything, let me know. If not, I'll pray for you. We all have days when we feel irritable or tired; this is normal. You have the right to feel this way. But remember, you are able to do whatever you put your mind to. Right now things may seem tough, but I know how capable you are of overcoming adversity. For now, express how you feel and let me know if I can help. But I will give you your space."

When I'm not hungry and I'm tired and frustrated with recovery

These are the hardest times because I'm full and I don't want to put anything into my mouth. But I know that I should eat, even if it's something small. Sometimes it's helpful to tell someone how tired I am of eating all the time when I don't feel like it. But I don't like it when all I get for an answer is, "Well, you are recovering from ED. Remember that!" Not helpful at all.

What *is* helpful is something like: "No one can make you eat. If you don't want to eat then you don't have to." WARNING! THIS DOES NOT WORK FOR EVERYONE! The only reason this works for me is that I am at the place in recovery where I can make myself eat, even if I really don't want to. When someone reminds me that no one can make me eat, I reflect and remember that recovery is for me—not for anyone else. If I don't eat, I will get tired and maybe end up in the hospital. I am the one who will suffer. On the other hand, if I decide to eat, life goes on and I can do whatever I want. So in the end, I obviously will eat.

But telling me that I must eat never helps. It makes me feel as though someone is forcing me into recovery when I've already decided to recover on my own. Of course, other victims do need someone to force them to eat. Some people with ED cannot decide to eat on their own, so this does not apply to everyone. But if you are able to eat on your own, taking control of your own recovery is worth it.

When I'm angry and wonder, "Why am I here?"

These days are tough because they make me question why I survived my fight with ED. Why am I still fighting? Why do I still have to be a victim of ED, be busy, stressed, etc.? We all have days when we wonder what our purpose is, why life has to be so tough.

I find it helpful when someone listens to me and lets me know that I'm not alone. "Marina, some days I feel the same way. I wonder why life has to be so hard and why I'm still here. But then I think back to all I've done and everything ahead of me. I remember that although I feel like this now, there are some good days when I feel happy and content. It's normal to feel like this. If you want to talk, I'm here for you. But remember how amazing you are, how successful you have been. And you have much waiting for you. You are a child of God and He never leaves you alone. Talk to Him and complain, and tell Him how you feel. You will find comfort in knowing that we all feel this way sometimes."

One very important thing to keep in mind during and after recovery is that things may take longer than expected to "normalize." What do I mean by normalize? You may notice that despite your recovery, life still isn't the way it used to be, nor is it the way you planned it to be. For example, you and your family may have thought that once you were weight-restored, all the ED thoughts and feelings would disappear. You might have hoped that as you ate, your hunger cues would return and you would be able to eat spontaneously. Unfortunately, this does not always occur. Even if you are at a healthy weight, you may still have times when you feel fat or do not want to eat. Certain events or conversations may trigger you, such as stressful circumstances or hearing about others dieting. Your hormones and neurotransmitters might not function properly. You may not feel perfectly happy and positive all the time.

So, what gives? Aren't things supposed to get better now that you are weight-restored and eating? I say this a lot, and it is worth taking the time to understand: *Recovery does not mean that life goes back to the way it was before ED*. While recovery does fix a lot of the damage of starvation, it might not necessarily fix everything (for example, some lost neurons might never be restored). However, keep in mind that this is not necessarily an unhopeful message.

In my experience, life did not go back to being exactly the same as it was before ED. Yes, there were some changes that perhaps we did not expect. For example, we stopped watching one of our TV shows, *The Biggest Loser*, because we realized that it could be triggering. We limited how many buffets we went to because buffets, too, triggered me. But now, I saw that I was a different person because of this struggle. I was wiser and stronger. My family changed, too. We went from being a family who never spoke about emotions to fostering an environment where feelings were expressed. We learned that there are no bad foods or good foods. We realized that the number on the scale should not dictate our happiness and self-satisfaction. It is normal to reflect on your experiences with ED and feel grateful for some things, but disappointed with other changes. It is okay if you notice that life is not "perfect" after recovery. Life will never be perfect—just human.

Something that struck me after recovery was how "off" my hunger cues were. Even after eating six meals a day, I still never felt hungry for years after recovery. This really bothered me because I felt that this should have normalized. Was there something wrong with my system? While I still ate by the clock, I found it frustrating that I could not rely on my stomach and brain to let me know when it was time to eat something.

Many patients tell me that they feel the same as well, even after being at a healthy weight for years. What's up with that? Well, it is obvious that ED numbs our hunger hormones and cues while we are sick. The interesting thing about this is that it may or may not return to normal after recovery. For some patients, it gets back to normal and they can eat when hungry. But for others like me, the desire to eat because of hunger simply did not exist. Why?

Let's think back to dopamine (DA), the reward neurotransmitter. Research shows that in ED patients, eating does not stimulate the release of DA as it should in normal people. This means that to a patient with ED, starvation literally "feels good," because in some twisted way, DA is now released when food is *not* eaten.[3] Interestingly, some patients, even after recovery, do not show normal DA release. Dopamine might not be released in response to eating for years after recovery, which means that a patient still will not feel pleased or happy when she eats. This could explain why the patient does not feel hungry after recovery—her brain doesn't feel rewarded by eating, so it is not a pleasurable activity.

If this happens to you, don't be discouraged, and don't let ED use this as an excuse to convince you to restrict again. Remember that even if your brain and body do not tell you when to eat, it is still your responsibility to eat enough. People do eat when they feel hungry, but they also eat if there is a special occasion, if they crave something, if they see free food (and why not? Food, and you don't have to pay—wow!), and so forth. ED may very well try to use your non-existent hunger cues against you; since you know this now, you should be able to recognize when ED is trying to ruin your recovery.

Don't forget to pamper and take care of yourself! Now that you have recovered, you deserve to live a happy and free life. Accomplish your

3   W. Kaye and G. Frank, "Overreactive dopamine receptors in anorexia nervosa," *Society of Biological Psychiatry*, 58 (2005): 908–12.

goals and pursue your dreams. You have restored your health and are now stronger and wiser. Don't let anyone bring you down or stop you from following your heart! You can do what you set your mind to. Always remember, though, that your body and health have top priority. If you are ill, you cannot achieve anything.

Your body gets you to places. Your strong legs keep you walking—even running, when necessary. Your strong heart pumps blood night and day to keep you alive. Your liver metabolizes substances and excretes toxic chemicals through your kidneys. Your lungs supply much-needed oxygen. Your arms lift up heavy things, and your hands write stories or type assignments. Your eyes see the beautiful things around you, and your ears hear the glorious sounds of nature. Your lips allow you to communicate with others, and your nose helps you smell the sweet scents around you. Your stomach digests the food that you eat, and your intestines do the same. Your reproductive organs make you female or male, and your muscles give you strength.

With an eating disorder, nearly all of this is impaired. Your muscles become weak, and it becomes harder to move, run, or exercise. Your heart becomes weak and finds it harder to pump blood effectively. Your brain cannot concentrate because it does not have enough nutrition; it thus becomes harder to concentrate. Your organs are lacking the nutrition that they need, so they shrink and cannot do their jobs. Your whole body slows down because it does not have what it needs: food. And without this food, your body cannot function.

It is time that we take steps to ensure that our bodies are not harmed—just as we do not want our cars scratched or damaged. We would never try to use our car on an empty tank, or neglect to fix a flat tire or a rust spot. Treat your body like your car—it deserves the best.

Chapter Nine

When you've mustard
the courage to recover by yourself

I have discussed how a family can support a patient in recovering from ED. But what happens when you don't have a family to help you? What if your family isn't there, or is not willing to support you? This is the focus of this chapter. However, I need to offer a big piece of advice, here: If your family is willing to help you, do not refuse this help. You will need all the support you can get.

But if you are forced to deal with this on your own, do not lose hope. It is possible!

All right, so you've noticed that there is something going on with your eating. You don't want to eat, and you've gotten a tad obsessed with your weight. You have a scale and check it frequently. You don't eat as much as you want to, but you convince yourself that you are full. You avoid eating at all costs, and you make excuses about why you cannot eat at the moment. Deep down, you know that this is not normal. Part of you wants to recover, but the other part of you is confused. If you eat, won't you gain weight? What was the point of all that restricting you just suffered through if you are going to start eating again? You want to eat, but you can't. You simply cannot put food into your mouth. You feel trapped. You are hungry, but you cannot eat. It is not even a choice—you feel compelled to starve yourself.

What to do? How do you find the strength within you to get medical attention and to start eating again? To be honest, this was where I was at first when I started recovery. My family wanted to help, but they did not know how. There was no time for me to educate them at first. I was frustrated with myself. I wanted to eat and get strong again, but I was so scared. One day, I decided that I would eat. I even went on the Internet and started to search for blogs about eating disorders and recovery. Yes, I knew I had an eating disorder. But I did not feel sick enough to get help. I thought that if I ate a little, I would be okay. It wasn't serious, I thought.

The Internet is not a safe place to find advice. I began reading forums of people with ED giving each other advice. I read how sick some people were, and this made me feel that I wasn't really as ill I had thought. I continued reading anyway, slightly interested that there were people around the world that struggled to eat like me. I read about how some patients made themselves vomit, while others simply refused to eat. Others said that recovery was a blast because they ate whatever they wanted. Still others complained that they had made a mistake by eating again because they gained a lot of weight. I was so confused. What was I supposed to do? For a while, I joined one forum and started asking questions. I asked strangers if I should eat. Some said yes, others said no. Other people told me that I would live with ED all my life so there was no use trying. Let this be a strong and clear message to anyone recovering from ED: The Internet is not a safe place to get advice about your health. You need medical attention. Do not listen to what people say online — they don't know you, and you don't know them.

After spending some time on this forum, I decided to try eating something one day. I planned that I would drink an extra cup of water the next day (yes, it was that bad. I was counting how much water I drank!). I had nightmares the entire night, worrying how much weight this would make me gain. The next day, I could not do it. I got a cup of water and refused to drink it. It was too hard. I could not drink or eat ever again. I was trapped in this endless spiral, and there was no way out of it. I would live the rest of my life without eating, eventually dying because of this. But I had no choice. ED would not let me eat or drink anything.

Over time, I lost weight. Eventually, I could no longer walk because my legs were too weak. My body had broken down all my muscles to create energy, and I was emaciated. But still I continued with ED. I would go to school and not eat all day. People would offer me food, but I declined. I made excuses like crazy — I am full, I already ate. I don't like eating apples. No, thanks. I had a big breakfast and am full now. Maybe later— I've already brushed my teeth.

How did I turn this mess around? To be honest, by the time I realized how ill I was, I was in the ICU on life support. Please do not let this happen to you. Do not make the same mistake that I did. Get help early. You are never "not sick enough" to get treatment for ED. If you try to eat but cannot, you have a problem. If you want to eat but are scared of gaining weight, you need help. The good news is that you can start off on your own. No one has to force you to get help because you can find the courage within yourself to seek treatment.

Making a decision to eat or to get help is one thing, but following through with it is a totally different story. You may want to eat, but ED will not let you. You want to get help, but you are scared. You do not want to gain weight—and you know that getting help means that you may have to. At this point, it is normal to feel anxious, angry, sad, or even depressed. This is a difficult time because it means having to go against ED. It means ignoring ED and getting help, even though you are not sure what "help" means. You are being brave. You are also doing the right thing. The longer you stay ill, the harder it becomes to get better.

The first step will be for you to see a doctor and explain what is going on with you. At this point, do not waste your time sugar-coating things. Tell the doctor what you are doing: how much you are eating, if you purge, etc. Be honest. You can get help only if you admit to what the problems are. Remember that the best treatment for ED illness is to break the cycle of starvation. The restricting needs to stop. It can be hard to admit that you have a problem, even if it is to yourself. A major issue that I had when ill was that I could not admit how ill I was. It was as though I had starved myself for so long that ED was an addiction. For me, restricting had become kind of like an obsession. I *had* to not eat because I *had* to lose weight. I had to lose weight because ED was so strong. I was scared of becoming fat. Unfortunately, I could not see how ill I was, and how much ED controlled me.

You may feel this way at first, too. You will probably feel that you are not sick enough to have ED, or that you can easily start eating when you "feel like it." But please, do not fool yourself. The longer you delay treatment, the harder it will be for you to recover.

No one should blame you. If your doctor will not listen to you, ask to be referred to a specialist in eating disorders. If you find a health professional who understands what is happening with you, that's great. The next step is to get weighed and get blood work. Common blood tests include complete blood counts, hormone panels, electrolytes, kidney markers, liver enzymes, and a glucose level. The doctor should also perform an ECG on your heart to see if it is functioning normally. This part may seem scary. You may want to turn back now while you have a chance. But you must stick with it. This is only the beginning; you are just getting started. Do not give up and let ED win again. A note of warning: if all your tests show normal results, it does not mean you are not sick. Remember that our bodies are extremely efficient at adapting to pressures, and death can occur suddenly, even if the person seems to be doing fine. A physician who knows about ED will know this. Again, if your doctor has had no experience with ED, get a referral to someone who has. You need this kind of support. If there aren't any experts in your area, your family doctor is your only option. It is okay. But whatever you do, make sure you are getting professional help. You cannot fight this battle without medical assistance.

Visiting a dietitian who understands EDs is your next step. The dietitian needs to understand that you have to eat to gain weight. Many dietitians, meaning well, will give you a meal plan that is full of fruits and vegetables. Don't get me wrong—these are important. But there is no way you are going to gain enough weight if you fill up on fruit. Your meal plan needs to have enough calories and protein and a great amount of variety. You need to be eating every three to four hours. You need to balance your meals with your physical activity. Make sure that the dietitian understands this.

Also, you should make a plan with someone to weigh you. This can be your dietitian or your family doctor, as you will be seeing them weekly for follow-ups. Whether or not you know your current weight really depends on you and the treatment providers who are helping you. Some patients do not like seeing their weight because it makes it harder for them to eat. Others feel that knowing their weight is important because they need to be exposed to it—although note that this might be ED trying to control your weight again. I am of the opinion that you should eventually know your weight because you need to get used to understanding that the number on the scale is just a number. It does not mean that you are good or bad. It does not define how beautiful or successful you are. Keep that in mind.

So, you have your meal plan and are at home. It is almost time to eat your meal, but you don't know how you are going to gather enough courage to do this. No one is around, so technically, no one will even know if you ate or not. You can always lie to your dietitian and doctor, right? Well, your weight will likely show if you are eating or not (although this is not always an accurate indicator). Some patients get around this by faking weight gains through the use of weights in bras, sand in shoes, etc. Do not let ED drive you to do this. Faking a weight gain is not helpful. It is prolonging your illness and strengthening ED. The longer you do not eat and the longer you are underweight, the worse this illness is going to get.

Now, your sandwich is staring at you. You know that you should eat. You told your treatment team that you would. But you can't. It is not even about a choice now. You are too scared, and ED is too strong. He is filling your head with being fat, ugly, and horrible. *Believe me when I say that this is the hardest part of recovery.* Eating when you don't feel hungry and when you are scared is literally the most challenging thing you will do in your life. But you must do it. Do not let ED win this battle. Stop ED in his tracks. Remember the distractions I mentioned earlier? Make use of these like crazy. When I was eating on my own at first, I turned on music, read a book, and had my favourite shows on TV (Disney cartoons all the way!). The first meal I ever ate in recovery was a tuna sandwich and a granola bar, plus an apple. I freaked out. I wanted to run away from the table and lie about eating. But deep down, I knew that I could not live like this for the rest of my life. I would have to eat someday, or else I would die at a very young age. I did not want to die! I had a life to live. I wanted to finish my degree and do great things! But for some reason, all this went out the door when I thought about eating. At that moment, I did not care about living a happy life. All I could think of was how I could not touch that sandwich. ED made me forget about all my hopes and dreams. The only thing that was on my mind now was this food and what I was supposed to do with it.

I blasted up my music. I watched Mickey Mouse dancing with his little friends. I read a few pages in my book. And then, I realized that an hour had gone by. I should have eaten this meal by now! The first thing that came to my mind was to skip it. After all, it was too late. If I ate now, my next meal would be too soon, or be pushed back. I had ruined the first day of recovery already! I told myself that I would start tomorrow, for real this time. But deep down, I knew that I was lying to myself. Something would happen tomorrow and I would make another excuse. It was now or never. I could not keep passing each day without eating and recovering. I had made the decision to get better, and that meant that I had to eat. I had to put in the effort into eating if I wanted to get better.

I thought back to how I had lived my days without eating. At first, it was hard. It was painful. I would be hungry all the time. But as time went on, it got easier for me. Maybe recovery would be like this, too. Maybe taking the first bite would be the hardest part. I would never know if I never tried. I had to take one bite at a time. So I did. I took the first bite. It was strange. I felt every inch of my body reacting as though it was fighting a battle. My stress response was activated, and my heart was racing. I felt dizzy and sweaty. I could not do this! I was freaking out. No! I would not eat! I would rather *die* than eat right now. I told myself to swallow, and then I would stop eating. I got the first bite down, and I felt like a mess. That was tough. I was shaking out of fear and panic. How could I eat this entire meal?

I got through it. One bite at a time. Lots of music. Episodes after episodes of my favourite TV shows. Phone calls to my friends who understood. Talking to people about anything that could keep my mind off of food. I'm serious. Go crazy! I used to talk to my friends about the newest baby pandas born at the zoo, the income of the Queen, how long it took to fly around the globe, etc. Whatever kept me eating and kept my mind off food. This is what you must do as well. Do not give ED a moment to take control over your mind. You must not give him a chance to slip back in and ruin your recovery. Take one bite, and then take another. Chew in between. You will get through this. You will recover. One bite at a time.

I did this for the first week, and I was exhausted. I was nervous about my weight. I had agreed to remove the scale from my room, but now I regretted that. I really wanted to know how much I had gained. I thought that I would have gained so much weight that this would be over. That I would be done and I could declare myself recovered. Of course, the first weigh-in was hell, to say the least. I had gained seven pounds in one week. I was furious! I blamed my dietitian for making me fat. I refused to ever eat again. I tried to recover, and this was the result? Once I had calmed down, I realized how foolish I had been. Yes, the weight gain was hard. But at the same time, I still had more weight to gain. And I knew that the first weight gain would be high because my body was dehydrated. As hard as it was to accept, I knew that I could not stop now. I had to keep eating. Whenever I doubted this, I reminded myself that recovery was like an experiment. If I hated this and if I was fat (which everyone assured me that they would not allow to happen), I could always go back to ED. I could start starving again. I had tried starvation and ED. Now it was time to try eating and recovery.

Remember this: You can always go back. Give recovery a try as an experiment. Do not give up right away, even if the weight gain is unbearable and eating is a battle. Do not stop. It gets easier.

This is not to say that you will suddenly love eating and that you will be free of ED. Rather, it means that you will find eating less of a chore. You will find it easier. You won't freak out each time you need to eat. You will grow accustomed to seeing the number on the scale go up, even if you do not like this. Whenever you have doubts about recovery, remember that this is your life. You can spend it starving with ED, or you can recover now and live life. What's your choice: life or death?

Eating in recovery will soon become a habit rather than a chore. You may not enjoy it, but remember that cancer patients do not enjoy chemotherapy, either. Nevertheless, it is what they need. The same goes for you: eating is what you need. Food is your medicine. There is no way to recover from ED without eating and establishing healthy eating patterns again, You cannot recover from ED if you are not at a healthy weight either. Follow up with your team and get support. Motivate yourself. When you feel sad and frustrated with recovery (as you will!), remember why you decided to recover. Remember how sad life was when you were hungry all the time. Remember how weak you were. You do not want to go back to that sad place and time. You want to live your life. Keep going forward and do not look back. Nothing, I repeat, NOTHING is fun or good about ED.

As you gain weight, you may find that you are ready to prepare your own meals. Your dietitian can help you with this. After a while in recovery, I felt confident in planning my own meals. At first, I did this and showed my plan to my dietitian. As I got stronger and my mind cleared from ED, I was able to do this with more efficiency. I was able to make my own meals and have them approved by my dietitian. Once I had maintained a healthy weight for some time, I stopped seeing my dietitian, but kept going to my doctor. Note that at this time, I was able to make my own meals, eat enough, and take care of myself.

You may not reach this point right away. Do not rush recovery, and do not let ED fool you into thinking that you are "cured" when you reach a healthy weight. That is one great accomplishment, but *recovery continues even after weight gain.* You need to ensure that you are indeed able to make meals without help. If you do this, do not forget to have your weight checked at the doctor's. This is important because you may think that you are eating enough when in fact you are not. Weight can fall off very quickly during this delicate time, and this can set you back in recovery. Even after you have reached a healthy weight, making sure that you are maintaining it is essential. This way, if you lose weight, you can catch it before you fall back into ED's hold. If you gain too much, your team can help you decide what to eliminate or exchange in your meal plan. In a sense, this fact helped me remain calm during recovery. Since I was being weighed weekly, I knew that I would not suddenly become fat. But remember that even if you are weight-restored, it is normal for weight to fluctuate from one to five or so pounds. This can be due to your menstrual cycles, stress, hormone levels, food intake, fluid intake, etc. Do not flip out suddenly if your weight this week is one pound higher than your goal. It is the trend that matters. This is another reason why you need to keep your appointments with your team.

As you recover and your weight increases, you will start to notice that your body is changing. I certainly realized that I looked heavier, and I was concerned that others would notice, too. At one point, I even refused to leave the house because I was worried that people would make fun of my new body. I wanted to hide from stores, schools, malls, and people. This is normal—after all, you have gained weight and you don't want people to comment on this! One helpful thing to remember is that although you have gained weight, you now look healthier. Remember this: you look *healthier*, not necessarily *heavier* or *fatter*.

In my experience, people did not comment on my new body. If someone did, it was usually to tell me that I now looked healthier and well. Of course, you will meet people who are not very kind and will somehow let you know that you have gained weight. This can be triggering, but if you anticipate it, it will not bother you. If someone tells you that you look as though you have gained weight, try to smile or walk away. Ignore the comment if possible. Whatever you do, do not let this get into your head and ruin your recovery. In fact, it does not matter what others say about your weight and new body.

You are healthier now, and that is all that matters. No one but you will die if you starve yourself. No one but you will benefit if you gain weight and are healthier. Ignore any comments that do not support your recovery. It is no one's business how much you weigh, how many pounds you have gained. ED will take any opportunity to sneak back into your life, even if this means using a comment against you. Be strong.

Therapy can be very useful and is often needed. A therapist who understands ED can help you work through your thoughts and feelings. Cognitive behaviour therapy is my "thing," because I strongly believe that our thoughts can influence our feelings, and our feelings can influence our thoughts. I have already talked a bit about this, and chapter thirteen has more information. If you can afford it or if your insurance covers it, I highly recommend that you find a therapist to help you. If you cannot, chapter thirteen has some useful tips that will certainly help you cope during recovery.

One final thing to keep in mind is that there is no "AHA!" moment in recovery. The fog will not suddenly clear up one day. You will not wake up one morning and be free of ED. Even years after recovery, you may still not enjoy eating. You may not love the way your new body looks. But you will learn to accept it. You will learn to love your body because it is strong and healthy. You will learn to appreciate how your stronger body allows you to live life to the fullest. Get rid of any triggers or reminders of ED. Stay strong in recovery and do not let ED back into your life. At the same time, do not wait for a revealing moment when you will feel "cured." This simply does not happen. But, over time, you will notice that ED has less of a hold on you. ED no longer fills your head with as many thoughts. You can eat without thinking about your weight and body. You can see the number on the scale and not be freaked out. You might not be a foodie, but you know when to eat and how much is enough.

This takes time, so be patient. You have come so far already. Do not let anything mess with your recovery. Do not let anyone tell you that you cannot recover.

Do not strive to be perfect, because no one is! Set goals that you can achieve, not goals that are far beyond what you can do. Do not become trapped in the never-ending cycle of perfectionism. I used to feel that I had to always be working, even if that is what I had been doing all day. It felt BAD to do "nothing"—as in, to take time off to do fun things, to play, to "chill" or to relax. I felt guilty when I *didn't* work or get 100 percent on all my tests. It was as if my brain was on all the time and simply did not want to turn off. It was not a fun experience. Sometimes I criticized myself for not being able to finish all my work. However, I realized that I had to let go of this perfectionism. You do, too. It comes down to this: What are you really trying to achieve? Is it reasonable? Are you trying to finish too much in such a small time period? Are you putting too many expectations on yourself that are unreasonable? If so, you need to STOP! Stop working and stop criticizing yourself. Stop being too hard on yourself. Throw perfectionism out the door and let things go—do not sweat the small stuff! Celebrate recovery and your new life. You have a second chance at life now. You are leaving ED behind. Throw a party—and do not invite ED.

I thought that once I recovered from ED, life would be so much easier. I thought that everything would be perfect and happy. That nothing would go wrong. But I was wrong. Don't misunderstand me—recovering from ED was the most important thing that I did. It gave me back my personality, my health, and my life. But that does not mean that life is "peachy-keen." Life is still full of its wild and crazy rides. I'm busy with school, I'm studying for exams, I'm trying to stay on track with recovery, I'm balancing my social obligations, etc.

But what really gets me is that I still struggle a lot. I'm pretty sensitive to things that happen around me: For example, I want everyone to be happy all the time. I try to avoid any arguments because I just want everything to be okay. It feels like since ED is not here anymore, nothing should go wrong or give me a hard time. I know that this is impossible. Recovering from ED is great but that does not mean that life will be perfect from now on. There are still so many problems . . . but that is life.

Which is what gets me annoyed. WHY IS EVERYTHING NOT BETTER? ED tries to tell me that since problems are still in my life, "recovery is not all that it is set out to be." He tries to convince me that recovery is not worth it, since life is still full of challenges. But I'm stronger now. And I know that this is not the case. Sure, life is not all perfect and happy now. But that does not mean that recovery is not worth it. Life is still hard, but I am stronger. Life is challenging, but I am determined. Challenges come and go, but I am more prepared to deal with them. Yes, life is not perfect now. But I AM BETTER NOW. That is the difference between my life now and my life a year ago. I have gone through so much and now see that although life is still hard, so many things are not. I am eating now. I no longer have to lie about my food intake. I am stronger now. I no longer have to worry about restricting. I have my old personality back now. I can laugh when I want to. I can make others laugh. I can be myself and love me for ME. So, life is definitely not always happy or easy. But no one said that recovery would change my life's circumstances. But recovery *did* change ME. It changed the way I am able to respond to the ups and downs of life. It changed the way I am able to look at challenges and accept them. It changed the way I feel about myself. It increased my chances of living a happy life.

Chapter Ten

Keep cookin' and eatin'!
You're so hot, you're bacon

You may be familiar with the term "relapse." Typically, it used to describe a state of falling back into a bad habit that you once overcame. In terms of ED, this means that you might start skipping meals and losing weight.

If this happens to you, you need to know a couple of things. First, relapses are normal. They happen. Recovery is hard work, and you cannot expect to be perfect. At the same time, once a slip occurs, it is important to notice it and to learn from it. This will make you stronger and better able to prepare for the future. But let us assume that you have already had a relapse. What to do?

Relapses are scary. Knowing that ED is coming back must scare you and make you feel confused. But it is great that you noticed this happening. That means you are more in control than ED is. Read that sentence again. YOU CAN DO THIS. Think about what ED wants you to do. Is he telling you to restrict? If he is, remember what happened when you restricted before? Sure, you may have lost weight and felt good—but did you REALLY feel good? Were you happy that you could not eat, when everyone else was enjoying life and food? Did your body always feel strong and able to do daily tasks? Probably not. So although restricting might feel good at the time, it does not feel good in the long run. It does much more harm than the temporary feeling of power that it may give you. Is ED telling you to count calories? Think about why this is so. If you are counting calories to ensure that you reach a certain (healthy) target each day, then that is all right.

For example, I cannot trust myself to eat enough just yet, so occasionally, I might look at the nutrition label to make sure that I am eating enough of that food to give me what I need. But, if you are counting calories because ED is telling you to only eat such a small amount, this is problematic. Think of how much time and effort this takes out of your day. And for what? To satisfy ED and make him claim victory over your life? It is not worth it! Food is good! All food is good in moderation. But when you start to restrict, ED will not stop. Today he will tell you to eat 400 calories. Then tomorrow, he will change his mind and tell you to eat forty calories. Then next to nothing. He does not stop. He will never stop until you are dead. I know that sounds harsh, but it is the truth. It is so hard to resist ED when he comes on strong. He is so witty, so smart, so cunning. He knows what gets to you and he will use that to get to you. If calling you fat will make you restrict, he will do it. If getting you to count calories will make you starve, he will force you to do that. Just remember this: If you give ED an inch, he will always take a mile. In other words, giving in to ED one day or a little bit simply gives him the chance to take more and more out of you. Do not let that happen. Show ED who is boss. You are in control.

How do you know if you are relapsing? It can be really hard to detect, especially because ED is so sneaky. Below are some of the signs to look out for, but in no way am I trying to say that these are the *only* signs. I am also *not* saying that if you see this, you (or the patient) are *for sure* falling back into ED. If you suspect that you or someone you know is relapsing, maybe it is time to investigate some more. These are some of the things that would give me a clue that ED might be trying to get back into his victim's life.

- Restricting foods that were previously enjoyed. This is a big one. If, for example, I absolutely LOVE chocolate (which I do, by the way), and suddenly, I start saying that I hate it . . . well, that would be a big clue that ED is trying to return. ED likes to make his victim "cut back" on foods that she enjoys, because to ED, enjoying food is WRONG. (And how sad is that?)

- Personality is showing signs of strain and/or smiles are diminishing. We all have days when things do not go so well, so we feel sad. This is not relapsing. What I am talking about here is a consistent, low, sad mood. A mood that tells you that this person is severely saddened, maybe even depressed. She looks tired, grumpy, and lifeless. This is a big warning sign because ED steals all joy and peace from his victims. When I was really sick, nothing could make me laugh — even the funniest shows that I used to enjoy.

- Instability of moods — as in crying over every little thing. Feeling hopeless and tired. Wanting life to end because there is nothing good about it. This makes sense when you think about what ED does to his victims. He robs his victims of everything good and enjoyable in life. Of course the poor victims will feel sad, weak, and hopeless! ED is a thief!

There are so many other signs, but these three really stood out for me, because I remember thinking about myself while sick and knowing that I had ED. I KNEW I WAS SICK, I just could not do anything about it. I was scared to eat, to get fat. I was tired and worried that if I admitted to having ED, I would get sent to the hospital. (Which I was, but not because I admitted that I had ED. I was sent to the hospital because I was on the verge of death.)

Sometimes, we might know when someone is relapsing into ED. If we know this, maybe we can help the patient before she falls deeper into ED's traps. At the same time, someone can relapse and not show any signs at all. Or maybe she shows the above signs but she is relapsing. Relapsing is difficult to detect, because patients with ED are all different in their symptoms. But, if you feel that you are relapsing, it is great if you can take the time to notice this and try to get help. When I feel sick and tired of eating, I tell my mom. I yell how much I hate eating. And then I still eat. It sounds weird, but it helps because then I feel as though I am letting my emotions out, but I am not letting ED win. Whatever you do, do not brush it off and let it continue. The earlier you seek help, the better your chances are that ED will not make you sick again. And don't be ashamed to admit that you need help — this is expected and anticipated. Relapsing does not make you weaker; in fact, admitting that you need help is a sign of responsibility and strength.

If you feel that you or someone you know is relapsing, you need to get help right away. Of course, it is always desirable to stop relapses before they actually occur and cause damage. There is no sure-fire way of doing this; however, there are some things that you, as a patient or caregiver, can do to prevent the relapse from getting worse. Here are some things that you should keep in mind about relapse prevention and recognition. A treatment team can help you anticipate and treat relapses as well.

● Know the signs that you might be heading for a relapse. This means different things for different people, and it also depends on what you are fighting against. With ED, I know that I am slipping when I have a bad day and feel fat, ugly, and useless. On those days, I really do not want to eat. But deep down, I know that skipping a meal might give ED power. So, what do I do? I move on with my day and eat my next meal. Granted, I will usually be angry and moody for doing this, but at least I have not allowed ED back in. If you struggle with drinking, maybe one day you will be out with friends and just want to have "a little drink." But you know that one drink can lead to two, which can lead to four, etc. — and before you know it, you have relapsed. What do you do? If possible, get out of the situation. Find others to be around, or do something else. Sometimes, the longer we are around temptations, the harder they become to fight. Remove yourself from the situation. It will help a lot.

If you cannot leave (or even if you can — it depends), take time to think about what is happening. How do you feel? Are you angry, tired, and stressed? When I feel ED coming back in, this is usually how I feel. I also feel trapped: My mind KNOWS that I should ignore these temptations from ED, but it is always easier to give in to them than to fight. But when I really think about it, although it may be harder to fight, it is what will benefit me in the future. When I feel fat because I ate, after a few hours I am able to think clearly. I know that

NOT eating would have been the easier thing to do, but it also would have given ED another chance to invade my life. EATING was harder, and more painful. But I know I did the right thing. And it makes me feel good knowing that I was strong enough to fight this battle. Know that every time you fight a temptation or urge to slip back into a bad habit, you are being heroic. I'm not kidding—that is hard work, and you succeeded!

● Reward yourself. Recovering or overcoming a challenge is always hard work. Without rewards, you are not likely to continue. Different people like different things, so find what works for you. When I am having a bad day, sometimes all I need is to take time for myself—to read, to blog, to play on my phone, to watch a funny show, etc. Maybe you like going to the movies, painting your nails, playing on the computer, or chatting on the phone. After you have relaxed, think about how awesome you have been. You did so well by resisting that temptation. You know that one slip is all it takes (sometimes) to slip back and have a full relapse. And you fought that. WOW! You are stronger now as a result of that experience. Any challenge—no matter how big or small—is always successful if you stay determined and committed. It always feels hard and stressful, but looking back now, you will realize that you made the right decision.

Remember that these slips happen. If you *do* happen to give in to the temptation, do not beat yourself up over it. Do not waste time thinking of "should, could, would." Instead, focus on what did happen. What did you do, and why did you do this? How can you prevent this from happening again? Do you realize that giving in might have set you back and possibly hurt your recovery or good habits? We all make mistakes, but what is important is to have the ability to look back and reflect on what we did—to learn from our experiences and to grow wiser and stronger. And if you need help or support from others, ask! My family and friends cannot fight ED for me, nor can they eat my meals for me. But they can be there to listen to me complain, to support me when I feel down, or to simply ask me how I am doing. There will always be someone there to help—just ask! God is there, too!

Something I found to be extremely helpful during recovery was to reflect on the benefits of recovery. This helped me to realize how much I gained from recovery, which allowed me to see my experiences with ED in a more positive light. It also brought to my attention how important it was that I not let ED back into my life. I recommend that you do this. However, don't be discouraged if you can't think of many benefits right away. It was not until I was in recovery for a solid amount of time that I could view my experiences with optimism. You may find it helpful to make a list and then add to it as you maintain your recovery. You will be surprised at how much you have learned, grown, and changed since you were ill. You will see that despite how challenging recovery may be, it is definitely worth the fight. Here are some things that I pinpointed as benefits of recovery:

🍎 FREEDOM and not worrying about food. To some extent, this is not true. I mean, I still need to worry about food in that I have to watch the time and eat by the clock. I still have to ensure that I am eating enough for what I need. But, it is so different from being sick. When I was sick with ED, I worried about food because I needed to find ways to avoid it. I had to think of excuses for why I was not eating, and to find ways to escape occasions that would require me to eat. Now, things are different. While I still cannot eat outside of the times I need to, I can go about my normal day without worrying about how to avoid eating. I prepare my meal and eat. Then life moves on. When I was sick, I could never calmly eat a meal. I still have days when I am sick of eating and tired of not being hungry, but this is what happens in recovery. I would choose this freedom over ED any day.

🍎 Being STRONGER. ED has taught me so much. One of which is how much I can handle. I was by no means able to survive my fight without God or the help of others. But it also took a lot of strength on my part. I learned that I am strong. I survived a long, terrible, sad journey in the

ICU. I thought I would never make it out alive, and there were times when I honestly wished that I would just die. But I pulled through, thank God. I now see how much motivation and dedication I have. I am a fighter. I will work hard to achieve my goals, and I will not let challenges take me down. Sometimes I may feel stressed, tired, or sad. But those are temporary lapses, and when I renew my strength, I can do anything I put my mind to.

🍎 Having better RELATIONSHIPS. When I was sick with ED, I always fought with my parents. They wanted me to eat; I refused. They told me I was too thin; I denied it. They wanted me to take a bite; I screamed. We were constantly angry at each other: They were angry because they were worried about me and did not know how to help; I was angry because I wanted them to stop telling me to eat. Now, things are *so* different. My parents are my best friends (and my sister, too!). I can tell them anything, and they support me no matter what. They provide me with everything I need, and even things I do not need! They love me unconditionally. I can talk to my mom about anything in the world. I do not need to hide things from her, like when I was sick (when I hid food, did not eat . . .). Looking back now, I realize how hurt they must have been when I was rude to them. It was not me, of course. It was the illness. ED made me mean to them because he wanted me to starve to death.

Now, I can honestly say that my parents/family are amazing. They helped and loved me even in my darkest times. The same with my friends — I now no longer need to hide things from them. I can go out with them, even if they are eating. If I have eaten my meal, I just sit with them, and we all feel fine. If it is time to eat, I will eat. No more lies, denying, or hiding. Life is good.

🍎 Having more ENERGY. When I was sick, I was convinced that I was still strong. This was not a lie — research shows that patients with chronic anorexia undergo changes that make their brains and bodies feel stronger. Basically, the body learns to adapt in times of starvation and thus is able to survive on small amounts of food (for a while, that is). So, I honestly did not feel tired. But now that I am eating normally, I feel the difference. I do not have to cope with sharp, stabbing hunger pains in my stomach. I do not have to drag my legs up the stairs because they are too weak to move. I do not have to ask for help when lifting heavy things because my arms and muscles are back. My hair is growing back to normal, as dark brown and wavy as can be. My eyes are as deep brown as they can get. My nails are strong and long. My skin is soft and smooth. My body is back. My life is back.

You may notice that after recovery, you are more aware of certain things in life. For example, you might pay more attention to other people's bodies and recognize when a person looks too thin. You may suspect that someone has an eating disorder because of the way she looks, acts, or eats. Be cautious with this. Not all people who have ED have overt symptoms that can clue you in on it. Some people may be thin for various reasons, such as physical illnesses or genetics. Others may be at a normal weight and still have an eating disorder. Whatever the case, don't jump to conclusions. Your experiences with ED have made you wiser, but don't make assumptions.

If you do feel that you want to give back to others and help raise awareness about eating disorders, make sure that you have been in recovery for a solid period of time. Being an advocate is great, but it also means that you may have to deal with triggering issues for others; or you yourself may become triggered. You need to be physically, mentally, and emotionally ready for this. Remember that not everyone who recovers from ED chooses to be an advocate—and that's okay. No one expects you to do this; in fact, your loved ones will be overjoyed if you can maintain your health and recovery.

Don't think that you need to appear in the media or write books to make a difference. You can make a huge difference in so many little ways, such as being a good role model for others, promoting healthy habits, etc. Can you help prevent ED from taking over people's lives? Probably not. But what you *can* do is to try your best to promote a way of living that embraces health in its full meaning. Whether you are a patient, a caregiver of a patient, or even someone who simply has an interest in eating disorders, there are small and subtle ways to make a difference. Always remember that these small things can make a big difference to someone. Here are some tips:

- 🍎 Be "normal" around food. What *is* normal, anyway? Well, to me, it means not making a fuss about food. This is hard in certain cultures like mine — Middle Eastern. For Arabs, food is the BEST. Going somewhere? We must eat. Visiting? Prepare food. Family gathering? Lots of food. So, for me, ED was even harder, because my family and culture did not have a neutral stance toward food. Do not get me wrong: it is wonderful to love food, and we all do! But in the home, the focus does not always have to be on food and weight. Parents, in my opinion, need to help their kids understand that their bodies need to be healthy and strong. This requires enough nutrition. Parents and children (and anyone else in the family) need to eat healthy meals. Moderation is key. Desserts should not be forbidden nor looked at as being a "reward."

    In fact, food should NEVER be used as a reward or punishment. For example, do not reward your child with chocolate for being polite, but then tell her that she cannot have it if she gets a bad mark in school. This reinforces the idea that chocolate is only for "good people." Instead, reward your child with other things: a toy, a game, etc. Teaching children that food is okay in moderation will help them learn to develop positive attitudes about food. Of course, teaching them that dessert in moderation is normal, too. A child cannot eat candy all day instead of healthy meals. In the same vein, a child should not be forced to eat fruits and veggies when everyone else is having dessert. What this means is that in the home, everyone should eat healthy foods, in moderate amounts and variety. If a specific health problem exists that needs certain foods, this is a different case.

🍎 Do not focus overly on physical appearance. This is hard, since society so often seems to do this. What I mean by this is that mirrors should only be used to make sure you look good before you leave to go somewhere. Do not stare at the mirror and think of what you do not like about your body. Do not compare yourself with others and wish you had a body like theirs. Accept yourself for who you are and how you look. You are special, and you are beautiful and handsome because you are in the image of God. Do not waste time criticizing yourself! Encourage others to do the same. In the home, this can mean praising your kids and others for what they do, not how they look. Sure, we all love compliments about our appearance, and this is GOOD and perfectly normal! However, we also need to be complimented on other things like our hobbies, talents, good deeds, ideas, and so on.

🍎 Recognize the signs of ED and take action. If you suspect this in someone, take action. Talk to her and calmly tell her how you feel. If you cannot, ask someone else to do so. Signs such as never eating, vomiting after every meal, losing too much weight, looking pale and ill, etc., are hints that someone might have ED. You might not always be right, but trying to help someone never hurts. I have spoken to many people about whom I was concerned, and it turned that they were fine — they just had a bit of disordered eating and needed to get back on track. At other times, people *did* have a problem, and talking to them helped. Of course, sometimes, people will not be open to discussing this. That is fine. At least you tried. Know the signs and watch for them.

There are many more, but these three are my main ideas. I hope this helps you to realize that while ED is not fully preventable, there are MANY things that we can do to ensure that we and our loved ones are safe, healthy, and happy. Of course, ED might still occur — even with all these interventions in place. But at least you will know that you have tried your best. And you will also know how to help victims and those who need more information. Knowledge is power. Learn about ED, become aware, and help others learn, too. It will make a BIG difference.

One excellent way to help prevent relapses is to acknowledge that recovery is a work in progress. Something that I noticed with myself is that I still need to be vigilant with my food intake. When I get busy with school and work, I tend to forget about how much I really need to eat to keep me healthy. But nutrition is always the top priority because I know that without a healthy body and mind, I cannot function properly. I learned that I need to plan my meals and make sure that I eat them. I noticed that during difficult times, I feel stressed and too lazy to get up and make my meals. I also feel exhausted and don't want to make a decision about what I am going to eat for dinner.

When I discussed this with my parents, we decided that it would be best if I continued to make a weekly meal plan. This way, I wouldn't have to make any last-minute decisions about my food, and I would be prepared to meet daily challenges. This is also a good way to ensure that you have all the groceries and items you will need for the week's meals. It may sound excessive, but you will be surprised at how many people (even without ED!) need to plan their meals. Furthermore, studies actually show that the patient with ED—even if she has recovered—has a hard time planning ahead.[4] While she can plan well in all other areas of her life, making decisions and plans about her meals and recovery is harder. Does this make the ED patient stupid or dumb? No. It is simply that her brain has not had to think about eating in so long. So, making plans for recovery is something new to her. And new things take time to get used to or to master.

What if I did not plan things out like this? Well, it would make me anxious. Let's say I did not plan that I would eat XXX for lunch. Then lunchtime comes around and I do not know what to eat. I am overwhelmed by all my options and so ED says, "*Well, I guess you can't because you do not know what to have, and deciding is too hard!*" SCORE: Me, nothing; ED, one. I do not want that to happen. So I make plans and pack my food with me. Or what about when I do not plan my meals and then I look in the fridge and I have run out of what I need? Do you think ED will tell me to go to the grocery store and buy it? NO! "*You don't have what*

---

4   S. Linder, F. Manfred, and Q. Norbert, "Decision making and planning in full recovery of anorexia nervosa," *International Journal of Eating Disorders* 7 (2012): 866–75.

you need to eat? Oh, well. I guess that means you cannot eat." Again, ED wins. So, by planning, I make sure that I am one step ahead of ED. I am prepared for all the challenges he might throw at me because I know that he will grab any small chance to make me slip back into his control.

While the brain chemistry of ED patients might show that there is some difficulty with planning, this does not mean that the patient is stupid or silly. It does not mean that she cannot make decisions. It simply means that her brain has been used to avoiding food, so it will take time to get used to it again. In the meantime, planning is the safest way to go. Plan your meals, what you will eat, when you will eat, who will make your food, etc. It may sound challenging and boring, but putting in about ten minutes to plan a week's meals will avoid the anxiety and stress of not eating and falling back into ED's traps. Ten minutes from my day planning my meals for the next week saves me a lifetime of health issues related to ED. Ten minutes of planning what I will eat for the week means that ED has NO TIME to try to convince me not to eat. Ten minutes of planning . . . that's all it takes.

Regardless of what you do to keep yourself safe, remember that the goal of recovery is to live life to the fullest and be healthy. You need to maintain a healthy weight, eat normally and enough, and have enough energy to meet life's demands. Younger patients may need more assistance from their caregivers in learning to master recovery. But no matter how old you are, you will always need help once in a while. Do not be ashamed to seek help or support when you need it. Try to reframe recovery: instead of looking at it as a chore or weakness, learn to see it as something that makes you unique. You have been through a terrible illness, but you have survived it. Don't feel angry if you still struggle with thoughts, meal planning, anxiety, depression, or anything else. We all have our own obstacles; what is important is that we learn to deal with them.

Think of ED (or any other illness) as a scar: you get hurt, you heal, but the scar is still there. It will be part of your past, even if it doesn't bother you now. It might not hurt you, but sometimes it can get annoying if it itches or if you are reminded of its presence. What about when it does itch or bother you, and you don't know how to stop it? That's when you seek the help of others (parents, friends, professionals) who can help put some lotion on it, massage it, or simply distract you so that you ignore it. But remember: that scar reminds you of how much you worked and fought to heal. And it shows the world that you are strong and had the will in you to push for your recovery. The scar might never go away, but as time goes on, you learn to deal with it. The scar is there. So what? You healed from it. Let it be there. It does not affect your life anymore. Over time, it will stop itching, and you will move on. Life will go on.

Chapter Eleven

Salami get this straight — men get ED, too?

Although I am a female who has struggled with an eating disorder, this is not to say that males do not succumb as well. Indeed, there seems to be a rise in the number of males affected by eating disorders. This is often referred to as "manorexia."

Many times, we focus on ED as being a "girl's issue" because we mainly see females as patients. Why? Perhaps a guy doesn't feel open to letting others know that he is struggling with this illness. We live in a world that tends to see females as being preoccupied with their bodies, whereas males are expected to have more important things on their minds. Hence, a male with ED won't want to be open about his struggles because he is worried that he will be ridiculed and teased for having a "girl problem." Can you see the problem here? Males may have ED but be ashamed to admit it, thereby delaying treatment.

Females will fall into ED because they want to be thin. But it is different for males: they may want to achieve "bulky" or muscular bodies. They may feel pressured to have "built" bodies, without fat. And they can manifest signs of ED in different ways. While a male might want to be thin, he may focus on exercising and building muscle. At the same time, he might not be open to discussing his problems about eating. This is of major concern because it means that he could be very sick, but no one is aware of this. Moreover, family doctors might not think of screening males for eating disorders.

How do males get treatment for ED? Like any ED, this needs help right away. But again, we must appreciate how hard it can be for a male to seek help. He might feel ashamed or concerned that he will be shunned for having ED. We need to remember that no matter who the patient is, ED is a difficult and life-threatening illness. It can kill patients very quickly. ED makes patients lose awareness of how much food is necessary to sustain life. Everything that has been written about ED in this book is the same for males. The differences may be in their symptom presentation.

There are many males who are ill with ED, and it is just as serious as it is for females. These males, like other patients, feel fat and horrid because of eating. They refuse to eat because they don't want to gain weight. In a male patient, the desire to be muscular may lead to overexertion in exercising. He may push himself to the limit to try to build muscles. In addition, he may tend to be more secretive about his eating habits. He fears letting others know about his struggles because he doesn't want people to think that he is weird, gay, feminine, etc. Family physicians also have a difficult time understanding why a male would have ED. It is not uncommon for doctors to tell patients with ED to "eat more and move on." This occurs with all patients but seems to occur more so with males. This is because some doctors don't see how males could have ED, so they assume that it's just a "phase" the patient is going through. Let me be clear about this: Any person with ED is not going through a phase; he or she is ill and needs to get help!

Another thing to bear in mind is that males who seek treatment for ED may feel alone in their struggles. Most treatment centres accept patients of both genders, but usually most patients are females. Therefore, when a male comes for treatment, he can feel isolated. If he is with an all-female group of patients, this could add to his discomfort. In treatment, natural-networker females may feel comfortable speaking with one another and sharing their feelings (although we are well aware that most patients with ED are not typically open to speaking about their illness), but a male might not feel comfortable doing that. He may also feel that he does not deserve treatment or is "odd" for being the only male in the group. This could deter him from seeking help in the first place or staying strong in recovery. As a result, even with treatment, males can have a harder time than females progressing in recovery.

Something that is common with male sufferers is having a lack of social support. Friends and family members may not understand why a male can have ED. Aren't eating disorders only for girls? What is wrong with this boy? Is he gay? Indeed, negative responses from families and friends will make it even harder for males to get help for ED. In addition, fathers of males with ED might not believe that their sons could have ED. A father may deny that his son has a problem because he does not understand how a male can be ill with an illness that mainly strikes females. This denial could hinder the male from getting help and add to the his distress.

Over the years, there has been hope that the stigma associated with ED would dwindle. While there has been some improvement with this, we are nowhere near where we should be. Patients still feel ashamed of having ED. In the past, males would have been very ashamed of admitting that they had ED — if they identified it as such at all — and would not have gotten help for it. Consequently, there may be adult males with ED today who did not get help when they were young.

Unfortunately, society still is not very supportive of people with ED, so this may continue to occur. It is important that all patients, including males, seek help for ED. We cannot wait for society to catch up and understand about ED. The time to get help is now.

Yes, you may feel shunned and you may feel angry for being teased because of ED. But at the end of the day, you are the one who is suffering and who is ill. No one will benefit from getting help except for you, and no one but you will suffer without treatment. Please, if you are a male or know a male who has ED, get help! Ignore what society says about ED, stigma, and gender. ED does not discriminate — it targets all patients! This means that all patients need help!

A common problem with all eating disorders is competitive sports. With females, this may be ballet or gymnastics or even hockey or football. But for males, sports such as wrestling or football can require them to be extremely muscular and fit. This competition may push some males to restrict intake and try to lose weight, or to use steroids or other substances to help them "bulk up." This can lead to eating disorders. Moreover, the competition and rigidity around sports and body shape can also be a risk factor. For example, a male may decide to start losing weight because his football coach told him that he needs to be thinner in order to be a better player. Along with the competition and comparing among team players, this can fuel ED and be extremely dangerous. Weight lifters might call this "bigorexia."

The media influences males as well as females. While we may think of the media as showing us only thin and tall women, there are also many stereotypical images of men. Males in magazines or commercials are thin, muscular, and well built. Those males are displayed as being rich, successful, and happy. These images can also fuel eating disorders. The desire to look like the male models in magazines or like celebrities can lead to restriction, weight loss, and obsession with one's body shape. Although this may not be spoken of often, there are indeed "ideal bodies" that have been set for males. If the desire to achieve this body becomes strong, ED may very well begin to develop.

How does a male with ED get help? If you are suffering, what should you do? You feel stuck: on one hand, you cannot live with illness all your life. On the other hand, you feel that no one will understand and you don't want people to tease you. This is indeed a difficult place to be in. Again, all that has been said previously in this book applies to males. A treatment team can help you recover and guide you along the way. Do not be ashamed to ask your family or friends for help if you feel that they will be able to support you.

Do not be dismayed at being a male with ED. It is not your fault, nor does this make you strange or "less of a male" than others. ED is a mental illness. You did not choose ED, ED chose you. You must take action and get help. Anyone can have an eating disorder. Being ill with ED does not mean that you are weird or strange. Do not be afraid to speak out and get help—it will save your life. More and more males today are becoming open to admitting that they have ED and are getting treatment. They have decided that they will not let their illness take control and kill them. Please, do the same. You are not alone.

Chapter Twelve

Feta up with obesity?

We've talked a lot about ED, but what about the other end of the ED spectrum—obesity? How can we be so concerned with anorexia eating disorders when there is an "obesity epidemic"? How can anorexia even exist when obesity is on the rise? A patient who struggles with ED fears that she will become obese as she recovers, as this is what society always seems to be concerned with in terms of food and weight. Professionals and parents may also worry that feeding a patient with ED will cause her to become overweight. At other times, a patient with ED may belittle her disorder because she feels that it is not as serious or as "bad" as being obese. The focus of this chapter is not to discuss obesity, nor its complications or treatment. Instead, it is to help patients, professionals, and caregivers understand that while obesity is on the rise, ED, when it occurs, is also problematic and must be treated.

First, let's discuss the "obesity epidemic." What in the world does this even mean? Typically, this phrase is used to describe the trend that obesity is increasing around the world. Notably, the increase in fast food portions and consumption, as well as the decrease in physical activity has contributed to this problem. Being at an unhealthy high weight is, in fact, also a big problem. Obesity is strongly correlated with many diseases, including heart attacks, stroke, hypertension, cancer, and more. Note the word *correlated:* this does not mean causation. What this means is that obesity is a *risk factor* for many illnesses, but it alone does not *cause* these problems. So, if obesity is such a big issue around the world, how can ED exist?

You may have heard that moderation is the best approach in all things. Indeed, that phrase is supported by evidence from countless sources. Eating too little can lead to ED, while eating too much can lead to obesity. But if obesity is more common than ED, why should we waste our time worrying about eating disorders? Well, you need to remember that spotting people who are overweight or obese is a lot easier than pointing out someone with ED. This is because someone may have ED and not be emaciated, and hiding weight loss is made easier when you wear baggy clothes. On the other hand, it is difficult to hide obesity. Thus, surveys for obesity are a lot more accurate than are those concerning EDs. Many people go to their doctors and complain that they want to lose weight, but how often do you see people begging for assistance in *gaining* weight? Not too often — patients with ED are not likely to see how they can be helped for their illness; it is easier to see help for obesity or weight gain.

As humans, we like to have reasons for occurrences and trends. The same goes with obesity. It is easy for experts to blame obesity on fast food, decreased activity, the usage of technology, eating bigger portions, etc. But what do we blame as the cause of ED? Some say that it is a genetic disease, others cite the media as being a problem, while still others are unsure. Indeed, it is hard to determine what causes EDs, since they are mental illnesses. On the other hand, we can likely point out things in our lives that have led to obesity or excessive weight gain. Therefore, we are more aware of obesity, and this is how the word gets around. In a similar fashion, we can use this knowledge to develop strategies to prevent obesity. We hear things about weight-loss programs, diets, reducing food intake, and more. But how we do stop ED? No one can give an answer to this puzzling question; hence, many experts, frustrated by this problem, ignore EDs and focus on what they *can* answer or be sure of.

How does one with ED survive in a world that is occupied with obesity and finding ways to lose weight? It is ever so difficult to remain strong in recovery when everyone else is concerned with weight-loss diets. The main thing to remember, which has helped me a lot, is that everyone is different. Some may need to lose weight; others may need to gain; while others simply maintain their weight. In my case, recovering from ED was hard when all my friends were telling me about their latest diets or weight-loss success stories. Every time I turned on the TV, I heard commercials about diets, exercise programs, and low-calorie meals. You can imagine how difficult this was! It triggered ED, inciting thoughts of frustration and anger. Why did I have to gain weight and eat when the entire world was trying to *lose* weight? I felt guilty, fat, and ugly. I had been there once, and this was why I decided to lose weight! And now that I had lost all that ugly weight, I was expected to gain it all back! This was not fair!

The key to recovering in a world obsessed with diets and weight loss is knowing why you are doing what you are doing. Are you recovering to become obese? No. Are you eating like a pig because you have no control over yourself? No. Do you plan on eating until you cannot fit through the door? No. You are eating now because your life depends on it. You are eating because you have lost so much weight that your body has become very sick. You are eating because right now, this is what you need to be healthy.

I used to scream that I would rather be skinny and unhealthy than be fat and healthy. But as I ate and recovered, I realized how wrong my thinking was. When I was ill and unhealthy, I could not do what I wanted. I was weak and could not live my life to the fullest. However, when I gained weight and maintained it within a healthy range, I regained my strength.

Obesity is a problem, and no one can deny that. As a nursing student, I am quite aware of what obesity can do to people, and I help patients lose weight if this is needed. But we must be clear about something: fast food did not cause obesity. This is certainly one factor that contributes to the problem, but this does not mean that food is bad. This is something that many patients with ED need to understand. I struggled with this: If food makes people fat, how in the world am I supposed to eat food and expect to stay thin? Food must be bad! Food is terrible! But think about this: Do all people who eat become obese? No. Does eating one meal at a restaurant make you obese the next morning? No. If you ate breakfast today, would you be obese tomorrow? No. This is something that patients with ED struggle to understand—food does not cause obesity on its own. In fact, why are we calling food good or bad? Food is food. That is all. It is not a reward, nor is it a punishment. It is what we all need to be healthy. Too much or too little food can cause health problems.

With the hype about obesity, it is easy to see how this can deter recovery from ED. Messages about weight loss, resolutions, and diets make it very hard for patients to maintain a healthy weight and keep eating. As an example, I was once eating a chocolate bar at school when one girl, not meaning any harm, asked me how I could do that without feeling guilty. She asked me how I could eat so much without worrying about my weight. I wanted to jump out of my skin! I *was* worried about my weight. I *did* feel guilty. I felt horrible! Yet, this is what I had to do to get better. Eating was part of my job now, and I had to do it if I wanted to live and be strong. Did this girl know that? Likely not. She did not mean to trigger me this way. But the damage had been done. I already felt horrible and disgusted with myself. She was right! How dare I eat chocolate when the world was avoiding such things to lose weight? How could I muster up the courage to walk in public and eat when the world was fighting to eat less? How could I be fighting to gain weight when society was struggling to lose it?

You cannot hide from society and avoid the world to recover. What you CAN do is avoid things that are not helpful. At first, I switched off the TV when diet commercials came on. I told my friends to not discuss their weight loss targets with me. We told my family not to make a big fuss over food and weight. But that was under our control. What about outside? I could not demand that all channels stop showing weight loss ads. I could not walk up to every individual at school and inform them that their conversation was triggering me. This is something that I had to learn to deal with. I had to understand that ED is a problem, but so is obesity. ED is my problem, and obesity is someone else's. ED is not more important than obesity, and obesity is not more important than ED.

What helped me stay strong in recovery was to reframe my illness, comparing it to cancer. If I had cancer and was going to chemotherapy, would I be angry that others did not have to do this? Probably. I would likely be frustrated that my medicine—chemotherapy—was painful. I would be angry that others did not have to go through what I was going through. But at the end of the day, if I did not take my medicine, I would die. It might not be fair that I am the only one who needs chemo, but it also is not fair that I will die if I don't take my medicine. If I had cancer, I would likely take chemo to prolong my life. No matter what happened or what others said, chemo would be my medicine and I would take it. Try to reframe ED in this way.

What happens when your family or friends are struggling with obesity? Here you are, eating your way through recovery, and others are losing weight. At lunch, you order a side of fries when everyone else has a salad. You have three snacks a day while others do not snack at all. You are trying to gain weight, while others are struggling to lose some. What do you do? How do you cope with this? Again, think of yourself only. Everyone has different needs to be healthy. Perhaps others need to lose weight for their health, or maybe they are just losing weight to fit into their bathing suits. But that doesn't matter now. You are not gaining weight "for fun"—you are doing this because your life depends on it.

Is obesity a problem? Yes. Is ED a problem? Yes. Both are extremes and are unhealthy. Both can lead to many complications. Neither is desirable. It is true that the world is concerned with obesity and may not devote enough time to ED awareness. However, this is not your problem now. Your task is to eat and become healthy again. You need to remain strong in recovery and ignore any advances that ED makes. Others may need to lose weight. Others may not need to do anything about their weight. Forget about others and their eating patterns. Forget about how much others weigh. Just focus on your own recovery.

Chapter Thirteen

CBT can help espresso your feelings

Remember when I mentioned cognitive behaviour therapy (CBT)? Even after being in recovery for a long time, you still may feel that therapy is useful. You don't need to have an active eating disorder to benefit from therapy. In fact, something like CBT can be useful for people at any stage of their lives because it helps us see the relationship between our thoughts and actions. Even though I have been in recovery for a while, I still feel that my thoughts can get the best of me. I have times when I need to calm down and reflect on how my negative thoughts are affecting my moods and outlook on situations. If you are seeing a therapist for CBT, you might consider continuing this for a while to benefit more from it.

When you are ill, you might not get the most out of therapy because your illness prevents you from putting enough effort into it. As you maintain a healthy weight, and your eating patterns normalize, you may find it helpful to start going to therapy again. If, however, there are reasons why you can't do this, such as time, money, convenience, etc., there are some exercises that you can do at home to help yourself. Your treatment team might also be able to recommend activities or useful resources. In any case, please consider doing some form of CBT. ED can really get the best of a patient and distort the way she thinks, which influences how she feels. Once you are no longer ill, you can begin to clearly see how this happens. Then you can take steps to fix this so that your thoughts can positively influence your feelings. You can also learn how to stop negative thoughts before they control your mood and negatively impact your life. Below I have listed some questions to think about, along with an example that I have used.

Consider these questions . . .

1. What are my thoughts about me or about this tough situation?

2. What makes me feel this way? What evidence do I have that this is true?

3. What evidence tells me that this is not true?

4. What would anyone else in this position feel like? What would they do?

5. How is this affecting my life? How do I wish I could feel right now?

6. What can I do to make myself realize that what I feel is not the best for me? Who can help me? What actions can make me feel in control/relaxed/happy?

If you think about a situation with these few questions in mind, you will start to realize where your feelings went "off the charts" and what you can do to fix it. I'll start with an example of my experience. Please try thinking about these questions the next time you are in a tough spot!

My situation: I am sad because I have gained a lot of weight during recovery.

1. I feel sad and angry. I am frustrated and feel ugly and fat. I am tired of working so hard.

2. I feel fat because I gained weight and my old clothes are tighter. I look bigger in the mirror. People tell me that I look BETTER, but this likely means that I am actually BIGGER.

3. Most of my (non-sick) clothes still fit me well—only the tiny clothes that I bought when ill are too small. And nobody actually *calls* me fat; they tell me that I look nice. I suppose

it is my own thinking that makes me feel fat and ugly. I am also stronger. I may have gained weight, but I also have more muscle now than when I was ill. The weight does not have to be all due to fat.

4.   Someone else who recovered from ED might also feel fat when she has gained weight. But over time, she would realize that she is not fat and that this is still ED. She would be proud of what she has accomplished and she would appreciate her new, stronger body.

5.   When I feel fat, I get angry and tired. I feel sad because I do not want to look different. Right now, I wish that I did not feel so lousy about myself. I wish that I felt like everyone else — that I did not care or mind about my weight and body size.

6.   To make myself feel better, I can look at question #3 — the evidence that does *not* support the issue. I know I am *not* fat; I have just gained weight. But I also look better — everyone tells me this, and I feel it, too. To help myself, I am going to ignore the bad thoughts from ED. When it gets too much, I will blog about it or share it with my mom (my best friend and supporter!). I can also keep myself busy so as not to give ED time to bother me. Also, I noticed that when I use my body for strength, I see how amazing it is. I can play sports with my friends and family without getting tired — something that I could not do when I was ill and thin.

There you go! It actually helped to write that down and reflect on it. Please try this at home the next time you feel down about something: work, friends, relationships, family, yourself, an event, etc. I guarantee that you will start to see things differently.

Now, let's assume that you are going through something difficult and you have already reflected on it using the above CBT questions. Perhaps the event is over or you are still going through it. But the important thing is, you feel awful. You feel hopeless, tired, and frustrated. You do not understand why in the world this is happening to you. What do you do? We will start with evaluating some thought patterns. What is a thought pattern? It is a way of thinking that can lead you to feel negative, hopeless, or frustrated. We *all* have moments when we feel this way, but the point of this exercise is to help you identify which ones you use most often so that you can also learn how to avoid them or solve this issue. There are many patterns that have been identified, but I will list a few here. As you read them, try to identify which ones you use or fall prey to. Below each one, I have written some tips/tricks to help you deal with or work through this pattern.

1. *Black-and-white (all-or-none) thinking.* Everything has to be perfect, or else I am a failure. I need to get 100 percent on my marks (or do very, very well), or else that means that I am stupid. I cannot make any mistakes or do anything (at all) wrong because that would mean I am a terrible person.

   Why does it have to be all or none? You can certainly do well on something without being perfect. And doing not-so-great does not make you a failure and mean that you are terrible. Instead, try to see what you can do differently the next time and how this can make things better. And try to realize that things are never perfect; you cannot expect that from others or yourself!

2. *Catastrophizing.* If something happens, it will be terrible! What's the worst thing that can happen? EVERYTHING! I am doomed. My life is over.

   One small mistake or bad event does not mean that it is the end of the world. Sure, it may have been bad. But you know that things will get better eventually. Thinking this way only makes you feel worse and it takes away energy that could be used for finding a solution.

3. *Ignoring the positives.* Nothing good is happening (or ever happens) in my life. Everything is terrible. There is nothing good about me, either. I have no talents, nothing to contribute, and I am a failure. My life is also hopeless.

   Think about what is GOOD about you or about the situation. What did you learn from this? Did this teach you about what you can do better next time? Can you see how this situation made you stronger? Do not let this one thing bring you down—you know that there are so many wonderful things about yourself! Encourage and motivate yourself to stay positive. You do not need to laugh when you are in pain, but you also do not need to make your situation worse by being hopeless.

4. *"Shoulding."* I should have done this instead of that. I should have said this, not that.

Thinking in this way can be helpful when reflecting, but often, we use this and then feel even more terrible. Instead of a "should have," try to reframe it: What would it have been better to do? Can I see why my action did not turn out well? What did I learn from this?

5. *Mind reading.* People think that I am stupid or silly. That man thinks I am ugly—he looked at me weirdly. That woman thinks that what I just said is dumb. My boss thinks I am a failure. My spouse thinks I am useless. My friends hate me.

You do not know what people are thinking. If you can, double-check by asking someone what his or her thoughts or feelings are. Try to remember that not everyone is focusing on you or thinking about how you look/act/feel. Most of the time, people might be looking at you but thinking of something else. Or maybe they are looking at something around you. If you have something to say, say it to the person to verify what you are feeling (e.g., "I feel that you are being mean to me today because of what I said to you yesterday. Am I right?").

Note that there are MANY more, but I chose these because I feel that they are the most common ones. Which do you use the most? To be honest, I think I fall prey to ignoring the positives (#3) the most. Now that you realize which ones you use the most, what can you do to fix this? What evidence supports this pattern? What evidence does *not* support it? Is this thought helping or harming your feelings and situation? How might someone else in this situation respond? What can you do to change this pattern or make things a bit easier to handle? Try to use these exercises to help you—not just when you are in a tough situation, but throughout your life. They are very useful tips to follow because they enable you to take control over your thoughts, which then affect your feelings and your life in general.

Another useful exercise for the patient is to write a letter to her eating disorder. This is helpful because it allows her to express her feelings about the illness, how it impacted her life, and what she learned from it. Note that this can be painful for some patients, so it might not be helpful for everyone. However, after being in recovery for a while, you may notice that by writing this letter, you are able to see how your experiences with ED have changed you. It is also a good idea to write the letter because it helps the patient see how the illness wrecked her life, but also demonstrates how she was able to overcome it. I found it to be a very empowering activity. I gave the letter to my parents, who said that it gave them insight into how difficult ED was for me. You don't have to share the letter with others, but if you want to, it might help them understand more about your experiences. Here is my letter. What does yours look like?

> ED,
> You have plagued for me a long time, perhaps for about seven years. When I was ill, you made me believe that you could make things better. That not eating and starving would stop people from teasing me and from making rude comments about my body. You made me think that starvation would make me look thinner and thus stop people from hurting my feelings. And sadly, I listened. I fell into your trap and I became very sick.
>
> Over the course of seven years, I became your slave. I ate very little food and lost weight. But each time I lost weight, it was never enough. You wanted me to lose more and more, to eat less and less. I did. Until I got so sick that I needed medical attention. I was dying, but I was blinded by you. The pressure you put on me to lose weight and not eat was unbearable. Food became the enemy, and anyone who told me to eat was also an enemy. You made me lie to my loved ones, pretending that I ate or was not hungry. But inside, the pain was real. I was hungry, but I could not eat for fear that I would gain weight.

It was hard for me to help people understand why I was struggling because it made no sense: Why couldn't I simply *eat*? But people did not know, ED, how mean you were to me. If I thought of eating just one more thing, you would haunt me, telling me that I was terrible. You would remind me of how people used to tease me, and you threatened that eating would make this all come back. I nearly lost my life because of you. I spent months in the hospital, too sick to do anything. My organs failed, my heart was weak, and I needed urgent care. I was in the ICU for about a month and a half, not aware of anything around me. Meanwhile, all who loved me suffered, not knowing if I would make it out alive. You probably were happy, ED, that I was dying. It would be one more victory for you, another life that you would have claimed. Another girl who innocently wanted to lose weight and look better, gone because of your torture.

I do not know how I survived. All I know is that the prayers of all my family and friends, along with God working through His powers and His people, got me through. I made it out of the ICU, with all my organs working properly.

But this made you angry. You could not leave me alone now that I had survived. You wanted to fight me more, to make me ill once again. Once I got out of the hospital, you continued to threaten that I would become fat. You made it so hard to eat, each time reminding me of how much weight I would gain. But I pushed through. I did not let you take over my life once again. With the support and love of my family, friends, and God, I ate. I fed myself, looking at the clock to see when it was time to eat. I ate, regardless of how full and ill I felt. I chewed through every meal with your taunting voice telling me how weak and useless I was. I watched as the scale went up and as my body changed.

In tears, I got rid of the old, smaller clothes and hated that I was gaining weight and eating. But inside, I knew that I was doing the right thing. I knew that giving you one more chance would kill me. So I kept fighting, trying very hard to ignore your teasing and demands.

And I still am fighting. I am recovering day by day. Yes, ED, it is still hard. It is difficult to eat when I am not hungry, and it is hard to see that my body is getting bigger. It is uncomfortable for me to feel that I am bigger than before and to see how much I eat. But when these feelings come, sometimes it helps to remember how much pain you caused me. I suffered for too long under your control. It is time that I took my life back, time to be free and live my life.

Recovery is hard work, and you do not make it any easier. But the things in life that matter—my health, school, happiness, family, and my faith—are what keep me going. I cannot say that you are out of my life for good, because then I would be lying. But I *am* saying that you no longer bother me like before. Yes, you call me fat and make me feel bad for eating and gaining weight. But that is all you can do to me, now. You cannot make me lie about food, starve to death, or restrict what I eat. I am stronger now and I have learned all your evil and cunning ways.

Maybe I was lucky to have survived you, but others are not. I know that you still haunt the lives of many girls, boys, men, and women out there. For some, you make them believe that they are not "sick enough" to get help. For others, you fight them so hard that they feel weak and cannot battle you. And sometimes, you do not have a person as a victim, so you make them feel fat and ugly so that you can make them fall.

Well, ED, I have a message for you. These people are not alone! They have people who love them and who care. I pray that they may find hope and strength to get rid of you and recover. I know, of course, that you will always be here. You are, unfortunately, one of the most dangerous illnesses out there. In fact, you kill more people than any other mental illness. But, I also want you to know that recovery is possible. People *can* and *do* and *will* get rid of you. Because you make our lives terrible. You plague us and make us feel worthless. And now, we are educated. We are unwilling to let you continue to take away our lives and the lives of those we love. Together, with education, awareness, prayers, and strength, we will overcome you. If that means gaining weight and eating, then fine. If that means ignoring your harsh comments, we will do it. If that means standing up for ourselves, then we are prepared. Whatever it takes, recovery is possible. It is not easy, but that is because it is a battle. We are up for that challenge. We will succeed.

You can also try formulating a list of what you learned from your experiences with ED. If you like this over writing a letter, go for it. I felt that doing both exercises helped me organize my thoughts. You will be amazed at the different things that you have learned. Your caregivers or family might also be interested in doing this because it can help them reframe their own experiences with the eating disorder and how the battle impacted *their* lives. Again, it helps to see how, despite being challenging, we have learned and grown as a result of this horrid illness.

Here is the list my parents and I made.

1. ED is a real, serious illness. I knew that I had an eating and body image problem, but I never felt that it would get so serious. I never believed it when people would say that ED could kill me—until I ended up in the ICU on a breathing machine, with dialysis, pneumonia, near heart failure, failing organs, etc. My journey with ED showed me how important it is for us to understand just how terrible and serious ED is. If anyone has ED or even a small problem with food, I suggest you address it right away. This can save lives. Do not think that your issue is too small or not important; it is.

2. Life is precious and too short to waste on ED. After nearly dying in the summer, I realized how amazing life is. Yes, it sucks when you are stressed and have so much to do. It also sucks when you feel trapped and frustrated. But at the end of the day, life truly is a blessing. I am so blessed to have a second chance at life. To spend time with the people I love, and to study and work at what I love the most (nursing, writing, helping others . . .). God has given me a second chance to live my life the way it should it be. ED wanted to kill me. I invite you all today to choose life over ED. You will truly feel free once you have made this choice and blocked ED out.

3. Food is good. YES! I said it! I like food. Who does not? ED made this hard for me to admit, and it still is hard for me to enjoy food, but sometimes, when I am having a good day, I realize how important and good food is. I like to eat certain

foods, and I certainly have favourite meals. At the end of the day, food is necessary for life. It makes us strong, it gives us energy, and it makes us happy.

4. There are *no* bad foods. Everything in moderation truly is all right. I would be very, very sad if I did not have my precious chocolates and carbs. At the same time, I would be lost without my yummy fruits and meats. All food is good. Our bodies need all types of foods. ED made me believe that I did not need to eat, and he made me "hate" certain foods. In recovery, I have challenged myself to try new foods, to taste different things, and to keep a variety of foods on my menus. This had helped me realize that I have favourite foods, and that variety is a good thing. Not all people are able to introduce variety right away in recovery. For some, eating alone is a big task. This was the case for me, but over time, I challenged myself. Today, I am blessed to say that I really do eat many different things.

5. People who love you should be held near and dear to your heart. As you know, I would not have made it through this journey without my family and friends. They visited me in the hospital every day, bought me flowers, prayed for me, kept me company. My loved ones make me feel special and support me—through the good and the bad. I am blessed to have them!

6. People who pour hate on you are a waste of time. No one in this world will be always happy with you. I have learned that it does not matter what others think. If they want to hate me and bully me, that is fine. That is their problem, not mine. I am not going to stop my life and ruin my recovery because of others. If they are rude or tease me, then it is they who have a problem. They need help. Meanwhile, I am going to simply pray for them, and hope that God gives them peace and turns them to the right path. I pray for their sake, that they might find comfort and stop hurting others. I hold no grudges against anyone. I will not aim to please others—it is a waste of my time. I will live my life the way God has intended me

to: healthy, happy, and in the right way. Haters can hate. I'll be mature and live my life being the best I can be; they can be immature and waste their time hurting others.

Now, what kind of CBT chapter would this be if we didn't address emotions and affirmations? As I mentioned before, a patient with ED may struggle with expressing and handling her emotions. She may not know how she feels or what to do about it. Using positive affirmations along with CBT can help you deal with the emotional roller coasters.

A positive affirmation is a statement that gives you strength, peace, comfort, or a sense of control and power. Simply put, we can say them to ourselves to make us feel good or to help us in times of trouble. I'm not suggesting that you say these out loud to yourself, although you can. But usually what I do is repeat some of these in my head when I feel overwhelmed. I've listed some of my favourite or most-used ones. You may have your own — use those as well! They truly help, but it takes practice. Sometimes, you might not even have the ability to believe what you are saying. But at other times, you can really think about what the affirmation says, and it can help a lot. They can also help you focus on what is happening, why, and what you can do about it.

When you feel angry

Affirmations:
Anger is a normal human emotion.
I am angry and that is okay.

Ask yourself:
Why am I angry? Should I be angry? What happened?
Am I angry with myself, with someone else, or because of something that happened?
Is there a solution to this problem?
Have I hurt someone because of my anger? Can I do something to fix this?
How can I calm myself down? (Take a walk, drink something, take deep breaths, etc.?)

When you are sad

Affirmations:
Nothing lasts forever.
Things always get better.

Ask yourself:
Why am I sad? Did something hurt me physically or emotionally?
Do I feel hopeless?
Can I find ANYTHING good in this situation?
Is there someone I can talk to? Do I feel misunderstood?
Am I lonely? Do I just want someone to be there for me, or to tell me that everything will be okay?
It might not be easy, but I need to look for a solution. What can I do about this?
Have I learned something new from this situation?

When you are stressed

Affirmations:
I feel stressed and that is okay.
I can handle tough situations.

Ask yourself:
What is happening? Why does this make me feel stressed?
How do I know that I am stressed? Do I feel hot, tense, sweaty, etc.? Is my heart beating fast? Do I feel dizzy or want to throw up?
Is there anything I can do to take some stress away? Can I use any relaxation techniques?
We all get overwhelmed. But the longer I feel stressed, the harder it will become. I need to think of ways to help myself, or to make the situation better.
Life is hectic, and we all get frustrated. I am not different. Can I remember a difficult time before? How did I handle it?

There are other emotions as well, but I am sure you get the general idea. Reorient yourself and try to take control over how you feel. Remind yourself that emotions are normal and human, but you should also try to think of ways to make yourself better. Find ways to express your emotions, though — this is very important. Sometimes, we do not always want solutions. Expressing our feelings is all we need. That is okay, because solutions can come later. Find ways to help yourself, or seek others to help you. Emotions become easier to handle and experience when you acknowledge your right to emotions, and you also feel better knowing that you *can* overcome this situation.

Finally, remember to be patient with yourself. Although CBT and other thought exercises are helpful, they can get frustrating or painful at times. They can evoke emotions or memories that you never thought even existed. Don't try doing all of these activities in one day. Rather, you may find it helpful to practise one each week. I highly recommend that you take the time to use these thought exercises, as you can benefit a lot from them. If possible, ask a loved one to complete them as well. If you feel comfortable, you can share your answers together — although this is not necessary. It is perfectly all right if you prefer to keep your answers confidential. Whatever you do, keep in mind that full recovery means that you can control the ED thoughts — it is not just about the weight and food. The powerful part about CBT is that it helps you realize how your thoughts and moods interact. This simple concept is essential if you are to stop ED from ruining your life again. By learning to "thought stop," you can shut negative thoughts out before they can harm you. You can also learn to "ride through" difficult emotions by utilizing distractions, deep breathing, yoga, or affirmations. You must learn that ED might try to get back into your life by putting thoughts, images, or feelings into your head. Your job in recovery is to recognize when that is happening, to put a stop to them, and to seek help.

The last thing we need to summarize is recovery itself. We've talked about it, but what exactly *is* recovery? People can define recovery in different ways, depending on their circumstances and beliefs. In any case, it may be helpful for you (or the patient) to define what recovery means. What does recovery look like to you? Writing this out or discussing it can be an eye-opener, and it might help you to see what areas of your life you need to work on. Below is my definition of recovery. How does yours compare?

● To me, recovery means freedom. It means waking up in the morning and not instantly thinking about my weight.

It means getting ready for my day and not worrying over what I will eat. It means that I can sit down for breakfast and enjoy my food. Recovery means that I can wear my clothes and feel beautiful simply because I am healthy. It means that I need not compare my body with anyone else's, because I am beautiful the way I am.

● Recovery means that my weight does not dictate how I feel about myself. It means that my clothes sizes are numbers, and nothing but that. It means that I can eat when I want to, not worrying about weight gain. It means that I enjoy my meals and can eat socially. I can enjoy all varieties of food—there are no good or bad foods. Recovery means that I can engage in physical activity without feeling compelled to do so.

● Recovery also means that I can recognize when ED is trying to get back into my life. It means that I acknowledge that I am not perfect, and that mistakes happen. I can ask for help when I feel that I would benefit from support. I can accept love and care from others. I can complete tasks without feeling the need to be perfect in everything. I can accept praise for my accomplishments because I realize that I have done a good job. I can enjoy my time with others without feeling nervous or trying to avoid meals. I can take risks and not worry that I will fail. I can make mistakes without feeling awful and dwelling on it for too long. I can learn from my experiences and use this to become a stronger and wiser individual.

● Recovery means that I do not deny that I have struggled with an eating disorder. I can acknowledge that this mental illness made me sick, but I can also see how I learned from it. I understand that I need to be vigilant lest ED try to fool me again. I am not ashamed of having been sick, and I am able to move on. I can express my emotions and learn to handle stress without relapsing. I can eat through the tears, pain, joy, and laughter.

● Recovery means that I am proud of myself. I know how far I have come, and I can see how hard I have worked to get here. I can pursue my dreams and accomplish my goals. I can use my talents and strengths to achieve great things. Life moves on, even if I am tired, angry, sad, or frustrated. I still eat, despite feeling that I have no appetite. I can open my wings and soar to new heights, not being afraid of falling time and time again. I will not let anyone tell me that I cannot do whatever I put my mind to—even if that person is me.

By now, you should know exactly what the recipe of recovery is. It just takes a few ingredients, but it does take some time. Nonetheless, I guarantee that if you use these ingredients and give it enough *time* to bake, you will have yourself one good-looking recovery.

Many plates of *food* (a variety is preferable—it makes recovery tastier)

One thousand dozen cups of *love* (feel free to add in extra hugs and kisses too)

Splashes of *determination* (it gives recovery that "zingy" taste)

Numerous pinches of *patience* (add as needed)

Sprinkles of *perseverance* (colourful or chocolate, whatever you like better)

Many ounces of *hope* (it makes recovery smell sweeter)

Liberal tablespoons of *support* (it holds recovery together so that it doesn't fall apart)

Dashes of *strength* (even if you run out, go buy some more—recovery is best with this!)

Now, mix all these ingredients into one bowl. Then, bake. By the way, don't worry about adding more of any of the above ingredients. Recovery always tastes better when you give it more flavour. Don't rush recovery as it bakes, though. It takes time. It's worth it.

Once recovery has baked, take a fresh slice and enjoy it, maybe with a cup of coffee or tea. Don't forget to relax! If you or someone you know is struggling with an eating disorder now, pass this recipe along.

Smell that? It is the aroma of recovery baking. Can't you just taste it?

Appendix

Feast on these resources!

There are certain things you should look for in an eating disorder treatment facility. Here are some things to consider when looking for a treatment centre or medical team for you or a loved one with an eating disorder:

1. How close is it to your house? Is it conveniently located so that your family can visit you?

2. How much will it cost? Do you have insurance that can pay for this? How much does insurance cover?

3. What is the treatment model that the facility uses? Do they believe that eating disorders are serious, mental illnesses? Do they blame the patient or family for the illness? Do they understand that ED is caused by many interacting genetic, physical, emotional, mental, and environmental factors?

4. Do the staff listen to patient and family concerns? For example, if as a parent you thought that your child was not progressing, would the staff be willing to listen to your opinions?

5. Does the facility advocate for family involvement? Do they allow visitors and family members to visit the patient and interact with them? What are the visiting hours and rules? Is there an opportunity for patients to eat meals with their

families and have a staff member/coach help the family support the patient?

6. Are families given support throughout this process? Is there education available to help families learn about eating disorders and how to support the patient throughout the recovery process? Are families empowered? Are parents encouraged to help their child overcome the eating disorder?

7. What are the treatment goals? How much weight should the patient gain? Is the food intake sufficient to promote adequate weight gain and restoration? Is the food edible and appealing? Is the patient's blood work monitored for complications?

8. How long is the patient expected to stay in treatment? Is there follow-up after the patient is discharged to ensure that she is on the right track?

9. What does the patient do with her extra time when she is not eating? Is she involved in group activities, work, or school? Is she given time to pursue her own interests, such as studying, drawing, reading, writing, etc.?

10. Is attention given to patient co-morbidities (depression, anxiety, self-harm, obsessive-compulsive disorder, etc.)? Is the patient taught how to work through her other psychological problems or challenges? Is she empowered to take control over her health and taught how to maintain recovery and prevent relapses?

11. How much choice are patients given about their treatment? If the patient is unwell, perhaps she should not be allowed to make choices about food intake or activity. However, if the patient is supposed to learn how to take care of herself, a certain amount of control should be given. Does the facility acknowledge that the patient might need tailored care and that eating disorders manifest in different ways for different patients?

Don't forget to educate yourself and others around you! Here are some resources that can be helpful for patients, friends, caregivers, and professionals.

http://www.nedic.ca
http://www.feast-ed.org
http://www.aroundthedinnertable.org
http://www.edbites.com
http://www.drsarahravin.com
http://www.kartiniclinic.com
http://www.maudsleyparents.org
http://www.edfofcanada.com

Most of the following books are intended for caregivers only; sufferers may not be mentally or psychologically prepared to handle the information.

Arnold, Carrie. *Decoding Anorexia.* New York: Routledge, 2012.

Brown, Harriet. *Brave Girl Eating.* New York: William Morrow, 2010.

Collins, Laura. *Eating with Your Anorexic.* New York: McGraw Hill, 2004.

Lock, Dr. David, and LeGrange, Dr. Daniel. *Helping Your Teenager Beat an Eating Disorder.* New York: The Guilford Press, 2004.

O'Toole, Julie. *Give Food a Chance.* Portland, OR: Perfectly Scientific, Inc., 2010.

About the Author

Marina Abdel Malak is a nursing student with an interest in medicine and mental illnesses. She is an active advocate for the National Eating Disorder Information Centre (NEDIC) and volunteers with many organizations. She loves to read, write, laugh, and learn new things. She has recovered from a seven-year battle with anorexia nervosa.

Marina enjoys travelling to various schools and organizations to speak about mental illnesses, ED, bullying, and medicine. Oh, and her favourite food is chocolate (just in case you want to share some with her — better chocoLATE than never!). You can follow her on her blog at **http://www. anorexiarecovery1.blogspot.ca**.

TO ORDER MORE COPIES:

GENERAL STORE PUBLISHING HOUSE INC.

499 O'Brien Road, Renfrew, Ontario, Canada K7V 3Z3

Tel 1.800.465.6072 • Fax 1.613.432.3634

www.gsph.com